100

MENTAL

MATHS

ACTIVITIES

YEAR

3

**Ann Montague-Smith
and Margaret Gronow**

Authors
Ann Montague-Smith
Margaret Gronow

Illustrations
Garry Davies and Mark Ruffle
(Beehive Illustration)

Series Designer
Sonja Bagley

Designer
Quadrum Solutions Ltd

Mixed Sources
Product group from well-managed forests and other controlled sources
www.fsc.org   Cert no. TT-COC-002769
© 1996 Forest Stewardship Council
FSC

Text © 2010 Ann Montague-Smith
and Margaret Gronow
© 2010 Scholastic Ltd

Designed using Adobe InDesign

Published by Scholastic Ltd
Book End
Range Road
Witney
Oxfordshire OX29 0YD

www.scholastic.co.uk

Printed by Bell and Bain Ltd, Glasgow

1 2 3 4 5 6 7 8 9   0 1 2 3 4 5 6 7 8 9

British Library Cataloguing-in-Publication Data
A catalogue record for this book is available from the British Library.

ISBN 978-1407-11417-0

The rights of Ann Montague-Smith and Margaret Gronow to be identified as the authors of this work have been asserted by them in accordance with the Copyright, Designs and Patents Act 1988.

Extracts from the Primary National Strategy's *Primary Framework for Mathematics* (2006) www.standards.dfes.gov.uk/primaryframework © Crown copyright. Reproduced under the terms of the Click Use Licence.

CONTENTS

Introduction

About the series

100 Mental Maths Activities is a series of six photocopiable teachers' resource books, one for each of Years 1-6. Each book offers a bank of mental maths activities, each designed to last between five and ten minutes. The activities are designed to fit the planning guidelines of the *Renewed Framework for Teaching Mathematics* (2007) and are therefore divided into five Blocks with three Units of work in each Block.

This series provides a valuable accompaniment to *100 Maths Framework Lessons* (Scholastic, 2007). The mental maths activities are designed to accompany lessons in the framework series and grids are provided at the start of each Block to indicate the lesson and page numbers of the associated lesson plans in the relevant *100 Maths Framework Lessons* book. Used together, the teacher will have a rich bank of resources, activities and questions, offering greater choice and variety, while keeping to a closely similar mathematical content and progression. It is for the teacher to decide when to repeat an activity and when to move on: the exact mix of consolidation and progression needed will vary from one class to another. However, the series is also wholly appropriate for independent use alongside any maths scheme of work.

The six Rs of oral and mental work

In addition to matching the content of the Renewed Framework, this series also reflects the six features of children's mathematical learning that oral and mental work can support identified by the Primary National Strategy when renewing the Framework. The 'six Rs' provide a valuable guide to the purposes of each starter and a 'type of starter' is offered alongside each of the activities in this book.

The six types of starter include:

- rehearse: practising and consolidating known skills

- recall: securing knowledge of facts - usually number facts

- refresh: drawing on, revisiting or assessing previous knowledge and skills

- refine: sharpening methods and procedures (eg mental strategies)

- read: using mathematical vocabulary and interpreting mathematical images, diagrams and vocabulary correctly

- reason: using and applying acquired knowledge and skills; using reasoning to draw conclusions.

For further information on the 'six Rs' visit the National Strategies website: *www.nationalstrategies.standards.dcsf.gov.uk.*

About the book

Each book provides support for teachers through 15 Units of mental maths, developing and practising skills that will have been introduced, explained and explored in your main maths lesson time. Few resources are needed, and the questions for each activity are provided in full. The books are complete with answers, ready for you to pick up and use.

The activities are suitable for use with single- or mixed-ability groups and single- or mixed-age classes, as much emphasis has been placed on the use of differentiated and open-ended questions. Differentiated questions ensure that all the children can be included in each lesson and have the chance to succeed; suitable questions can be directed at chosen individuals, almost guaranteeing success and thus increased confidence.

Several essential photocopiable resource pages are also included (see pages 88-95). These resources are listed alongside each activity where required and should be prepared in advance of each mental maths session.

Each activity in this book has one or more learning objective based on the Year 3 teaching programme in the Renewed Framework. Curriculum grids are presented at the start of each Block to assist teachers with their planning and to highlight links with the related *100 Maths Framework Lessons* title. Alongside the activity description, required resources are highlighted, as well as the 'type of starter' (see above for further information). Where appropriate a 'mental strategy' for solving a number sentence or problem is suggested. Discussion of the children's methods is encouraged, since this will help the children to develop mathematical language skills: to appreciate that no single method is necessarily 'correct' and that a flexible repertoire of approaches is useful; to improve their overall confidence as they come to realise that all responses have value. Strategies are encouraged that will enable the children to progress from the known to the unknown number facts, thus developing their ability to select and use methods of mental calculation.

In Year 3, emphasis is placed on strategies for addition and subtraction (especially with numbers up to 50), adding from the larger number, counting up for a small difference, partitioning and using doubles and near doubles. Repeated opportunities for counting in twos, fives and tens will help to develop the children's understanding of patterns in times tables. The relationships between different times tables are also used to support learning of new tables. Some lessons are based on simple fractions and their equivalents, telling the time and exploring number patterns. Games are included in each term's work to help provide variety and generate enthusiasm for numbers. Open-ended questions are used to challenge the children and extend their thinking.

Transitional assessments

Transition is a time when, historically, children dip in their performance. Why this occurs is open to discussion but schools are increasingly aware of the need to accurately track children during these periods in order to ensure, as far as possible, a smooth learning journey. Transitional assessment is therefore important not just as a tool for summative judgements at the end of a school year, but also for communicating with teaching colleagues across the school.

100 Mental Maths Activities Year 3 includes three photocopiable single-level transitional assessments for levels 2 and 3, which will provide evidence of where children have reached in relation to national standards. Printable tests, mark schemes and answer sheets are available on pages 96-111.

BLOCK A

Unit 1

100 Mental Maths Starters				100 Maths Lessons		
Page	Objective	Activity title	Starter type	Unit	Lesson	Page
8	Read, write and order whole numbers to at least 1000 and position them on a number line; count on from and back to zero in single-digit steps or multiples of 10.	① HTU chart	Read	1	2	10
9	Multiply one-digit and two-digit numbers by 10 or 100, and describe the effect.	② Place value (×10)	Refresh	1	5	11
9	Derive and recall all addition and subtraction facts for each number to 20, sums and differences of multiples of 10 and number pairs that total 100.	③ Spider maths	Refine	1	6	12
10	Derive and recall all addition and subtraction facts for each number to 20, sums and differences of multiples of 10 and number pairs that total 100.	④ Find the target	Recall	1	7	13
10	Add or subtract mentally combinations of one-digit and two-digit numbers.	⑤ Count on	Rehearse	1	9	14
11	Add or subtract mentally combinations of one-digit and two-digit numbers.	⑥ Take away	Refresh	1	10	15

Unit 2

100 Mental Maths Starters				100 Maths Lessons		
Page	Objective	Activity title	Starter type	Unit	Lesson	Page
12	Partition three-digit numbers into multiples of 100, 10 and 1 in different ways.	⑦ Place value (×100)	Refresh	2	1	21
13	Derive and recall all addition and subtraction facts for each number to 20, sums and differences of multiples of 10 and number pairs that total 100.	⑧ Quick adding	Recall	2	3	23
14	Multiply one-digit and two-digit numbers by 10 or 100, and describe the effect.	⑨ Counting in tens	Recall	2	4	23
15	Derive and recall multiplication facts for the two-, three-, four-, five-, six- and ten-times tables and the corresponding division facts; recognise multiples of 2, 5 or 10 up to 1000.	⑩ Steps of 4	Recall	2	5	24

■SCHOLASTIC

Unit 2 ...continued

	100 Mental Maths Starters			100 Maths Lessons		
Page	**Objective**	**Activity title**	**Starter type**	**Unit**	**Lesson**	**Page**
15	Add or subtract mentally combinations of one-digit and two-digit numbers.	⑪ I say, you say	Recall	2	7	26
16	Add or subtract mentally combinations of one-digit and two-digit numbers.	⑫ Near doubles	Refine	2	9	27

Unit 3

	100 Mental Maths Starters			100 Maths Lessons		
Page	**Objective**	**Activity title**	**Starter type**	**Unit**	**Lesson**	**Page**
17	Round two-digit or three-digit numbers to the nearest 10 or 100 and give estimates for their sums and differences.	⑬ Round up, round down	Rehearse	3	1	33
18	Add or subtract mentally combinations of one-digit and two-digit numbers.	⑭ Check it out	Refresh	3	3	35
19	Develop and use written methods to record, support or explain addition and subtraction of two-digit and three-digit numbers.	⑮ Mental addition	Reason	3	5	36
20	Derive and recall multiplication facts for the two-, three-, four-, five-, six- and ten-times tables and the corresponding division facts; recognise multiples of 2, 5 or 10 up to 1000.	⑯ Multiples of 2, 5 and 10	Rehearse	3	7	38
21	Use practical and informal written methods to multiply and divide two-digit numbers (eg 13 × 3, 50 ÷ 4); round remainders up or down, depending on the context.	⑰ Target products	Rehearse	3	8	39
22	Solve one-step and two-step problems involving numbers, money or measures, including time, choosing and carrying out appropriate calculations.	⑱ Double up	Recall	3	10	40

BLOCK A

① HTU chart

Resources
An HTU chart enlarged to at least A3 size (from photocopiable page 88); a pointer

Learning objective
Read, write and order whole numbers to at least 1000 and position them on a number line; count on from and back to zero in single-digit steps or multiples of 10.

Type of starter
Read

Answers
1. 702
2. 408
3. 304
4. 901
5. 607
6. 801
7. 505
8. 48
9. 91
10. 73
11. 64
12. 36
13. 517
14. 125
15. 931
16. 619
17. 252
18. 724
19. 411
20. 835

Count along the top row of numbers on the chart. Then point to individual numbers for children to read out.

Combine numbers by pointing (eg 200 then 3, for children to say 'two hundred and three'):

1.	700	2		11.	60	4	
2.	400	8		12.	30	6	
3.	300	4		13.	500	10	7
4.	900	1		14.	100	20	5
5.	600	7		15.	900	30	1
6.	800	1		16.	600	10	9
7.	500	5		17.	200	50	2
8.	40	8		18.	700	20	4
9.	90	1		19.	400	10	1
10.	70	3		20.	800	30	5

SCHOLASTIC

(2) Place value (× 10)

Learning objective	Resources
Multiply one-digit and two-digit numbers by 10 or 100, and describe the effect.	A board or flipchart

Type of starter
Refresh

Write H T U on the board with a 6 in the units column. Ask: *What number is 10 times larger than 6?* Ask an individual child to write the answer on the board. Emphasise that the 6 has moved across the 'boundary' from units to tens and that the 0 acts as a 'place holder'. Repeat by asking: *What number is 10 times larger than 60?*

Write each starting number and ask for a volunteer to multiply it by 10:

1. 9
2. 90
3. 2
4. 20
5. 8

6. 5
7. 30
8. 7
9. 10
10. 4

Answers

1. 90
2. 900
3. 20
4. 200
5. 80
6. 50
7. 300
8. 70
9. 100
10. 40

(3) Spider maths

Learning objective	Resources
Derive and recall all addition and subtraction facts for each number to 20, sums and differences of multiples of 10 and number pairs that total 100.	A board or flipchart

Type of starter
Refine

Mental strategy
Remind the children that addition can be done in any order.

Write a target number (eg 10) in the middle of a 'spider' diagram. Ask the class to suggest different ways of making that amount. Start with addition. Now, use subtraction, using facts that start with a number up to 20.

No set answers

BLOCK A

④ Find the target

Resources	Learning objective
A board or flipchart	Derive and recall all addition and subtraction facts for each number to 20, sums and differences of multiples of 10 and number pairs that total 100. **Type of starter** Recall

Answers

1. 3 + 7
2. 8 + 3
3. 8 + 3 + 6
4. 6 + 8 + 7
5. 8 + 7
6. 8 - 6
7. 7 - 3
8. 8 - 6 + 7
9. 7 - 3 + 8
10. 8 - 6 + 3

Write the numbers 6, 8, 3, and 7 on the board.

Ask the class to take some or all of these numbers and use addition and/or subtraction to make given totals (eg 16 = 7 + 6 + 3):

1.	10	6.	2
2.	11	7.	4
3.	17	8.	9
4.	21	9.	12
5.	15	10.	5

⑤ Count on

Resources	Learning objective
None	Add or subtract mentally combinations of one-digit and two-digit numbers. **Type of starter** Rehearse **Mental strategy** Ask: *What is 26 more than 3?* to demonstrate that it is easier to put the larger number first and then count on by the smaller number.

Answers

1.	29	6.	46
2.	38	7.	45
3.	35	8.	60
4.	31	9.	30
5.	41	10.	59

1.	What is 25 more than 4?	6.	What is 7 more than 39?
2.	What is 32 more than 6?	7.	What is 42 more than 3?
3.	8 add 27	8.	52 add 8
4.	7 add 24	9.	21 add 9
5.	What is 5 more than 36?	10.	53 add 6

(6) Take away

Learning objective	Resources
Add or subtract mentally combinations of one-digit and two-digit numbers.	None
Type of starter	
Refresh	

Use these questions to practise subtraction with the class:

1.   Take 9 from 12.

2.   Find the difference between 18 and 13.

3.   11 minus 5.

4.   Find the difference between 8 and 6.

5.   How many more is 16 than 7?

6.   Take 5 from 14.

7.   Subtract 3 from 15.

8.   19 minus 12.

9.   How much more is 20 than 7?

10.   Subtract 8 from 11.

11.   Find the difference between 17 and 4.

12.   8 minus 8.

13.   How much less than 13 is 3?

14.   Find the difference between 10 and 1.

15.   5 minus zero.

16.   Subtract 7 from 18.

17.   19 minus 13.

18.   How much more is 14 than 6?

19.   Take 6 from 17.

20.   How much less than 15 is 9?

Answers

1.   3
2.   5
3.   6
4.   2
5.   9
6.   9
7.   12
8.   7
9.   13
10.   3
11.   13
12.   0
13.   10
14.   9
15.   5
16.   11
17.   6
18.   8
19.   11
20.   6

⑦ **Place value (× 100)**

Resources	Learning objective
A board or flipchart	Partition three-digit numbers into multiples of 100, 10 and 1 in different ways.
	Type of starter Refresh
	Mental strategy Shift the digits two places to the left to multiply by 100.

Answers

1. 300
2. 3000
3. 400
4. 4000
5. 700
6. 600
7. 5000
8. 900
9. 2000
10. 800
11. 500
12. 1000
13. 100
14. 4000
15. 8000

Write Th H T U on the board with a 6 in the units column. Ask: *What number is 100 times larger than 6?* Ask an individual child to write the answer on the board. Emphasise that the 6 has moved across the 'boundary' from units to hundreds and that the zeros act as 'place holders'. Repeat by asking: *What number is 100 times larger than 600?*

Write each starting number and ask for a volunteer to multiply it by 10:

1. 3
2. 30
3. 4
4. 40
5. 7
6. 6
7. 50
8. 9

9. 20
10. 8
11. 5
12. 10
13. 1
14. 40
15. 80

BLOCK A

(8) Quick adding

Learning objective	Resources
Derive and recall all addition and subtraction facts for each number to 20, sums and differences of multiples of 10 and number pairs that total 100.	None
Type of starter	
Recall	

This is a rapid recall session for pairs of numbers with totals up to 20. Ask the children to raise their hands to answer individually.

1.   2 + 2

2.   5 + 5

3.   10 + 10

4.   13 + 1

5.   16 + 2

6.   7 + 3

7.   8 + 2

8.   14 + 3

9.   15 + 2

10. 8 + 7

11. 7 + 6

12. 8 + 9

13. 9 + 4

14. 13 + 6

15. 6 + 14

16. 3 + 12

17. 4 + 14

18. 13 + 4

19. 12 + 6

20. 11 + 8

Answers

1.   4
2.   10
3.   20
4.   14
5.   18
6.   10
7.   10
8.   17
9.   17
10. 15
11. 13
12. 17
13. 13
14. 19
15. 20
16. 15
17. 18
18. 17
19. 18
20. 19

BLOCK A

(9) **Counting in tens**

Resources	Learning objective
None	Multiply one-digit and two-digit numbers by 10 or 100, and describe the effect.
	Type of starter
	Recall
	Mental strategy
	Suggest that the children use a mental number line of tens to find count on/back numbers.

Answers

1. 60
2. 50
3. 70
4. 130
5. 120
6. 140
7. 200
8. 190
9. 210
10. 230
11. 130

Explain that you would like the children to count in tens, starting from zero, and that you will beat time to keep a steady pace. Start the count and after a few decade numbers, stop the count. For example, on 60 and ask:

1. What number did you just say?

2. What is the ten before 60?

3. What is the ten after 60?

Continue the count from the last number said. This time continue to beyond 100 and stop the count on 130. Ask:

4. What number did you just say?

5. What is the ten before 130?

6. What is the ten after 130?

Continue to 200 and ask:

7. What number did you just say?

8. What is the ten before 200?

9. What is the ten after 200?

10. Count on in your heads from 200 for three tens. What number do you say?

11. Count back from 200 for seven tens. What number do you say?

Repeat this, stopping on different decade numbers.

Steps of 4

Learning objective Derive and recall multiplication facts for the two-, three-, four-, five-, six- and ten-times tables and the corresponding division facts; recognise multiples of 2, 5 or 10 up to 1000. **Type of starter** Recall	**Resources** A board or flipchart
Count together in fours from 0 to 40 and back again. Write the four-times table on the board as the children say it. Recite it together. Divide the class into groups of four. The first group starts with '1 times 4 is 4'. The second group continues and so on. Some of the answers can be removed from the board as the count continues.	**No set answers**

 # I say, you say

Learning objective Add or subtract mentally combinations of one-digit and two-digit numbers. **Type of starter** Recall	**Resources** None

As a class, the children say the complementary number that makes the total up to 20:

1. I say 12, you say…
2. I say 9, you say…
3. I say 5, you say…
4. I say 16, you say…
5. I say 10, you say…
6. I say 18, you say…
7. I say 15, you say…
8. I say 7, you say…
9. I say 11, you say…
10. I say 20, you say…
11. I say 14, you say…
12. I say 6, you say…

Answers
1. 8
2. 11
3. 15
4. 4
5. 10
6. 2
7. 5
8. 13
9. 9
10. 0
11. 6
12. 14

BLOCK A

12 **Near doubles**

Resources	**Learning objective**
A board or flipchart	Add or subtract mentally combinations of one-digit and two-digit numbers.

Type of starter
Refine

Mental strategy
Write 14 + 15 = 29 to show that the answer is equal to double 14 plus 1.

Encourage compensating up or down as necessary.

Write 19 + 21 = 40 to show that a difference of 2 means the number in-between can be doubled.

Answers

1. 13
2. 17
3. 25
4. 39
5. 31
6. 37
7. 43
8. 49
9. 33
10. 29
11. 16
12. 22
13. 50
14. 42
15. 26
16. 36
17. 80
18. 30
19. 60
20. 24

1. 6 + 7
2. 8 + 9
3. 13 + 12
4. 20 + 19
5. 15 + 16
6. 18 + 19
7. 22 + 21
8. 25 + 24
9. 16 + 17
10. 15 + 14

11. 7 + 9
12. 10 + 12
13. 26 + 24
14. 22 + 20
15. 14 + 12
16. 17 + 19
17. 41 + 39
18. 16 + 14
19. 29 + 31
20. 11 + 13

(13) Round up, round down

Learning objective
Round two-digit or three-digit numbers to the nearest 10 or 100 and give estimates for their sums and differences.

Type of starter
Rehearse

Mental strategy
Suggest that the children imagine the number line for the number said, such as 41. Ask them to look at their mental image and decide where the number lies: closer to 40 or closer to 50.

Explain the convention for rounding tens: a number ending in 1 to 4 rounds down, a number ending in 5 to 9 rounds up.

Now tell the children that you will say a number. Ask them to decide whether it rounds up to the next ten or down.

Ask them to write their rounded number on their whiteboard. When you say 'Show me', they should hold up their board for you to see.

1. Round 17.

2. Round 24.

3. Round 39.

4. Round 41.

5. Round 84.

6. Round 55.

7. Round 63.

8. Round 92.

9. Round 9.

10. Round 99.

Resources
Individual whiteboards and pens

Answers
1. 20
2. 20
3. 40
4. 40
5. 80
6. 60
7. 60
8. 90
9. 10
10. 100

BLOCK A

(14) Check it out

Resources	Learning objective
A board or flipchart	Add or subtract mentally combinations of one-digit and two-digit numbers.

Type of starter
Refresh

Mental strategy
Emphasise that the order of addition has no effect on the answer.

Encourage 'convenient' pairings (eg numbers making a multiple of 10, doubles or near doubles, adding a 'near multiple of 10' and then adjusting).

Answers

1. 16
2. 29
3. 18
4. 31
5. 19
6. 24
7. 31
8. 39
9. 71
10. 50

Write each of the questions below on the board and ask for the answer. Discuss some of them.

1.   6 + 3 + 7

2.   12 + 9 + 8

3.   5 + 4 + 9

4.   21 + 6 + 4

5.   7 + 7 + 5

6.   9 + 6 + 9

7.   12 + 13 + 6

8.   16 + 19 + 4

9.   31 + 30 + 10

10. 15 + 17 + 18

▲SCHOLASTIC

⑮ **Mental addition**

Learning objective	Resources
Develop and use written methods to record, support or explain addition and subtraction of two-digit and three-digit numbers.	A board or flipchart
Type of starter Reason	

Write: 18 + 25 = and 27 + 27 = on the board. Allow the children a minute to work out the answers.

Discuss the methods used. Gather (or if necessary, suggest) methods such as: beginning with the larger number and then using complementary addition; partitioning; using doubles; dealing with units first.

Write the following and discuss methods:

1. 16 + 36 =

2. 24 + 26 =

3. 35 + 26 =

4. 23 + 33 =

5. 28 + 14 =

Answers

1. 52
2. 50
3. 61
4. 56
5. 42

(16) Multiples of 2, 5 and 10

Resources	**Learning objective**
None	Derive and recall multiplication facts for the two-, three-, four-, five-, six- and ten-times tables and the corresponding division facts; recognise multiples of 2, 5 or 10 up to 1000.

Type of starter
Rehearse

Mental strategy
Count in twos, fives and tens with the children.

Remind the children of the patterns in each table (eg all multiples of 2 are even numbers; five-times table products end alternately in 5 and 0).

Answers

1. 8
2. 25
3. 30
4. 100
5. 30
6. 16
7. 4
8. 15
9. 70
10. 50
11. 20
12. 20
13. 50
14. 18
15. 5
16. 40
17. 6
18. 40
19. 10
20. 12

1. 4×2
2. 5×5
3. 3×10
4. 10×10
5. 6×5
6. 8×2
7. 2×2
8. 3×5
9. 7×10
10. 10×5

11. 4×5
12. 2×10
13. 5×10
14. 9×2
15. 1×5
16. 4×10
17. 3×2
18. 8×5
19. 1×10
20. 6×2

(17) Target products

Learning objective	Resources
Use practical and informal written methods to multiply and divide two-digit numbers (eg 13 × 3, 50 ÷ 4); round remainders up or down, depending on the context. **Type of starter** Rehearse	A board or flipchart

Write the numbers 2, 3, 4 and 5.

Ask the children to multiply two or more of these numbers to 'hit' the target totals:

1. 10

2. 20

3. 40

4. 15

5. 30

6. 24

7. 60

8. 120

9. 6

10. 12

Answers

1. 2 × 5
2. 4 × 5
3. 5 × 2 × 4
4. 3 × 5
5. 5 × 3 × 2
6. 3 × 4 × 2
7. 4 × 5 × 3
8. 3 × 4 × 2 × 5
9. 2 × 3
10. 3 × 4

(18) **Double up**

Resources	Learning objective
None	Solve one-step and two-step problems involving numbers, money or measures, including time, choosing and carrying out appropriate calculations.
	Type of starter
	Recall

Answers

1. 14
2. 12
3. 8
4. 4
5. 18
6. 10
7. 16
8. 0
9. 4
10. 14
11. 6
12. 2
13. 12
14. 8
15. 20
16. 18
17. 0
18. 10
19. 6
20. 16

A quick recall session.

1. twice 7
2. add 6 to itself
3. 2 times 4
4. double 2
5. twice 9
6. double 5
7. 2 times 8
8. add 0 to 0
9. twice 2
10. double 7

11. 2 times 3
12. add 1 to itself
13. twice 6
14. add 4 to itself
15. double 10
16. add 9 to itself
17. double 0
18. twice 5
19. add 3 to 3
20. add 8 to itself

Unit 1

100 Mental Maths Starters				100 Maths Lessons		
Page	Objective	Activity title	Starter type	Unit	Lesson	Page
25	Represent the information in a puzzle or problem using numbers, images or diagrams; use these to find a solution and present it in context, where appropriate using £.p notation or units of measure.	(19) Silver start	Rehearse	1	1	45
26	Derive and recall all addition and subtraction facts for each number to 20, sums and differences of multiples of 10 and number pairs that total 100.	(20) Add three or more numbers	Reason	1	4	47
26	Identify patterns and relationships involving numbers or shapes, and use these to solve problems.	(21) Half of half	Refresh	1	5	48
27	Relate 2D shapes and 3D solids to drawings of them; describe, visualise, classify, draw and make the shapes.	(22) 2D or 3D?	Refine	1	6	49
27	Derive and recall multiplication facts for the two-, three-, four-, five-, six- and ten-times tables and the corresponding division facts; recognise multiples of 2, 5 or 10 up to 1000.	(23) Steps of 3	Rehearse	1	11	53
28	Derive and recall multiplication facts for the two-, three-, four-, five-, six- and ten-times tables and the corresponding division facts; recognise multiples of 2, 5 or 10 up to 1000.	(24) Count in fives	Rehearse	1	12	53
28	Use knowledge of number operations and corresponding inverses, including doubling and halving, to estimate and check calculations.	(25) Number families	Recall	1	14	54
29	Use knowledge of number operations and corresponding inverses, including doubling and halving, to estimate and check calculations.	(26) Double up	Recall	1	15	54

Unit 2

100 Mental Maths Starters				100 Maths Lessons		
Page	Objective	Activity title	Starter type	Unit	Lesson	Page
29	Solve one-step and two-step problems involving numbers, money or measures, including time, choosing and carrying out appropriate calculations.	(27) Work it out	Rehearse	2	1	62
30	Derive and recall multiplication facts for the two-, three-, four-, five-, six- and ten-times tables and the corresponding division facts; recognise multiples of 2, 5 or 10 up to 1000.	(28) More 2 ×	Recall	2	3	63

Unit 2 ...continued

	100 Mental Maths Starters			100 Maths Lessons		
Page	Objective	Activity title	Starter type	Unit	Lesson	Page
31	Represent the information in a puzzle or problem using numbers, images or diagrams; use these to find a solution and present it in context, where appropriate using £.p notation or units of measure.	(29) What's the problem?	Reason	2	4	5
32	Identify patterns and relationships involving numbers or shapes, and use these to solve problems.	(30) Addition grid	Refine	2	6	66
33	Relate 2D shapes and 3D solids to drawings of them; describe, visualise, classify, draw and make the shapes.	(31) Imagine this shape	Read	2	7 or 8	66-67
33	Draw and complete shapes with reflective symmetry; draw the reflection of a shape in a mirror line along one side.	(32) Lines of symmetry	Reason	2	9 or 10	68
34	Read and write proper fractions (eg 3/7, 9/10), interpreting the denominator as the parts of a whole and the numerator as the number of parts; identify and estimate fractions of shapes; use diagrams to compare fractions and establish equivalents.	(33) Number fractions	Refine	2	12	70
34	Read and write proper fractions (eg 3/7, 9/10), interpreting the denominator as the parts of a whole and the numerator as the number of parts.	(34) Half and quarter	Refresh	2	14	71

Unit 3

	100 Mental Maths Starters			100 Maths Lessons		
Page	Objective	Activity title	Starter type	Unit	Lesson	Page
35	Represent the information in a puzzle or problem using numbers, images or diagrams; use these to find a solution and present it in context, where appropriate using £.p notation or units of measure.	(35) Money puzzles	Reason	3	1	78
35	Derive and recall all addition and subtraction facts for each number to 20, sums and differences of multiples of 10 and number pairs that total 100.	(36) Mental subtraction	Reason	3	2	78
36	Derive and recall multiplication facts for the two-, three-, four-, five-, six- and ten-times tables and the corresponding division facts; recognise multiples of 2, 5 or 10 up to 1000.	(37) Table talk	Recall	3	4	79
37	Use knowledge of number operations and corresponding inverses, including doubling and halving, to estimate and check calculations.	(38) Doubles	Recall	3	5	80
38	Identify and estimate fractions of shapes; use diagrams to compare fractions and establish equivalents.	(39) Shape fractions	Refresh	3	6	81
38	Solve one-step and two-step problems involving numbers, money or measures, including time, choosing and carrying out appropriate calculations.	(40) Twice as much	Rehearse	3	11	85
39	Relate 2D shapes and 3D solids to drawings of them; describe, visualise, classify, draw and make the shapes.	(41) Matchstick shapes	Recall	3	13	87
40	Identify patterns and relationships involving numbers or shapes and use these to solve problems.	(42) Properties of 2D shapes	Read	3	15	88

(19) **Silver start**

Learning objective
Represent the information in a puzzle or problem using numbers, images or diagrams; use these to find a solution and present it in context, where appropriate using £.p notation or units of measure.

Type of starter
Rehearse

Resources
Large pictures of silver coins and a £1 coin

Tell the children that they can use only silver coins and the £1 coin to answer the following questions.

1. Name the four silver coins.

2. How many 50p coins are equal to a £1 coin?

3. How many 50p coins equal £2?

4. How many 50p coins equal £3?

5. How many 50p coins equal £5?

6. How many 10p coins are equal to one 20p?

7. How many 10p coins equal two 20p coins?

8. How many 10p coins equal three 20p coins?

9. How many 10p coins are worth the same as a £1 coin?

10. How many 20p coins are worth the same as a £1 coin?

11. How many 20p coins equal £2?

12. Which three silver coins equal 50p?

13. How many 5p coins equal 10p?

14. How many 5p coins equal 20p?

15. How many 5p coins equal 50p?

16. How many 5p coins are there in £1?

17. Make 50p using four coins.

18. Make 50p using five silver coins.

19. Which three coins total 75p?

20. Which four coins total £1.45?

Answers
1. 5p, 10p, 20p, 50p
2. 2
3. 4
4. 6
5. 10
6. 2
7. 4
8. 6
9. 10
10. 5
11. 10
12. 20p, 20p,10p
13. 2
14. 4
15. 10
16. 20
17. 20p, 10p, 10p, 10p
18. 20p, 10p, 10p, 5p, 5p
19. 50p, 20p, 5p
20. £1, 20p, 20p, 5p

(20) Add three or more numbers

Resources	Learning objective
A board or flipchart	Derive and recall all addition and subtraction facts for each number to 20, sums and differences of multiples of 10 and number pairs that total 100.
	Type of starter Reason
	Mental strategy Stress that making 10 (eg 3 + 7) and changing the order (eg 3 + 5 + 7 = 3 + 7 + 5 = 10 + 5) can be useful strategies when adding three or more numbers.

Answers

1.	16	6.	20
2.	13	7.	20
3.	14	8.	19
4.	12	9.	16
5.	18	10.	17

1. 2 + 8 + 6
2. 9 + 1 + 3
3. 5 + 4 + 5
4. 7 + 2 + 3
5. 8 + 6 + 4

6. 2 + 8 + 3 + 7
7. 9 + 1 + 6 + 4
8. 8 + 2 + 3 + 6
9. 4 + 3 + 6 + 3
10. 2 + 7 + 5 + 3

(21) Half of half

Resources	Learning objective
None	Identify patterns and relationships involving numbers or shapes, and use these to solve problems.
	Type of starter Refresh

Answers

1. 50, 25
2. 100, 50
3. 44, 22
4. 200, 100
5. 40, 20
6. 30, 15
7. 400, 200
8. 60, 30
9. 120, 60
10. 80, 40

Find half and half again of:

1. 100
2. 200
3. 88
4. 400
5. 80

6. 60
7. 800
8. 120
9. 240
10. 160

(22) 2D or 3D?

Learning objective
Relate 2D shapes and 3D solids to drawings of them; describe, visualise, classify, draw and make the shapes.

Type of starter
Refine

Mental strategy
Some children might not know the name of the 'hemisphere'. Encourage them to describe its properties until they can relate it closely to the sphere.

Resources
One copy of '2D or 3D?' (from photocopiable page 89) per child; individual whiteboards and pens

Ask the children to write the name of each shape on their whiteboards. Check for any common difficulty in naming any of the shapes.

Continue by asking individual children to give at least one property of each shape. Ask other children to raise their hands if they can add another property – even if they cannot name the shape. Write these properties on the board underneath the name of each shape. Properties might include:

Triangle
A polygon with three corners (or vertices). A shape with three sides.

Cuboid
A solid shape with six rectangular faces. All angles are right angles.

Hexagon
The hexagon has six sides. All sides are the same length and all angles are the same size.

Prism
The end faces of a prism are all identical. If you cut a prism along its length it always has the same face.

Hemisphere
The base of a hemisphere is a circle. It is half a sphere.

Pentagon
It is a five-sided flat shape (or polygon).

Answers
1. Triangle
2. Cuboid
3. Hexagon
4. Prism
5. Hemisphere
6. Pentagon

(23) Steps of 3

Learning objective
Derive and recall multiplication facts for the two-, three-, four-, five-, six- and ten-times tables and the corresponding division facts; recognise multiples of 2, 5 or 10 up to 1000.

Type of starter
Rehearse

Resources
A pencil and one copy of '1–100' square (from photocopiable page 90) per child

Ask the children to draw a line through all the multiples of 3 up to 60 on the 1–100 square. When the children have finished, count together in threes to 60 and back again. How far can the children go without looking at their 1–100 squares?

Write the three-times table to 30 on the board. Ask the class to say it together.

No set answers

BLOCK B

 24 # Count in fives

Resources	Learning objective
None	Derive and recall multiplication facts for the two-, three-, four-, five-, six- and ten-times tables and the corresponding division facts; recognise multiples of 2, 5 or 10 up to 1000.

Type of starter
Rehearse |

Answers

1. 15
2. 30
3. 45
4. 35
5. 60
6. 20
7   50
8. 25
9. 40
10. 30
11. 15
12. 35
13. 45

Start by asking the children to count on in fives to 100 from: 25, 60, 80, 55, 30, 45.

How many more to 100 from:

1. 85 (suggest 3 'steps' of 5 = 15)
2. 70
3. 55
4. 65
5. 40

Find the product of:

6. 4 × 5
7. 10 × 5
8. 5 × 5
9. 8 × 5

10. 6 and 5
11. 3 and 5
12. 7 and 5
13. 9 and 5

25 # Number families

Resources	Learning objective
A board or flipchart	Use knowledge of number operations and corresponding inverses, including doubling and halving, to estimate and check calculations.

Type of starter
Recall |

Answers

Two addition and two subtraction statements for each number family. For example:

9 + 6 = 15

6 + 9 = 15

15 – 9 = 6

15 – 6 = 9

Write the following numbers on the board: 6, 7 and 13. Ask for two addition statements using all of these numbers. Then, ask for two subtraction statements using all of the numbers.

Ask for all four statements using each of these number families:

1. 9   15   6
2. 18   12   6
3. 17   8   25
4   10   50   40

5. 13   21   8
6. 16   27   11
7. 25   13   12
8. 20   30   50

26 # Double up

Learning objective	Resources
Use knowledge of number operations and corresponding inverses, including doubling and halving, to estimate and check calculations.	None
Type of starter Recall	

Make sure the children are familiar with various words and phrases that mean 'doubling' (eg twice, 2 times, double, add a number to itself).

1. 2 times 4
2. Double 5
3. Twice 11
4. Add 1 to itself
5. Twice 7

6. Double 10
7. Twice 13
8. 2 times 8
9. Add 11 to itself
10. Add 14 to 14

Answers

1. 8   6. 20
2. 10   7. 26
3. 22   8. 16
4. 2   9. 22
5. 14   10. 28

 27 # Work it out

Learning objective	Resources
Solve one-step and two-step problems involving numbers, money or measures, including time, choosing and carrying out appropriate calculations.	None
Type of starter Rehearse	

Discuss some of these problems, asking for the strategies used.

1. I think of a number, then subtract 4. The answer is 6. What was my number?
2. I think of a number, then add 7. The answer is 16. What was my number?
3. My friend and I together spend 50p. He spent 30p. How much did I spend?
4. A spider has 8 legs. How many legs do 2 spiders have? 5 spiders?
5. Insects have 6 legs. How many legs would 3 ladybirds have? 10 ladybirds?
6. I have £2 to give to four children. They will each have the same amount. How much will that be?
7. Peter saved 50p a week for 6 weeks. How much did he save?
8. 80 crayons are put into packets that hold 10 crayons each. How many packets will be needed?

Answers

1. 10
2. 9
3. 20p
4. 16, 40
5. 18, 60
6. 50p
7. £3
8. 8

BLOCK B

(28) More 2 ×

Resources	Learning objective
None	Derive and recall multiplication facts for the two-, three-, four-, five-, six- and ten-times tables and the corresponding division facts; recognise multiples of 2, 5 or 10 up to 1000.
	Type of starter
	Recall

Answers

1. 6
2. 14
3. 8
4. 2
5. 12
6. 20
7. 4
8. 18
9. 10
10. 16
11. 3
12. 7
13. 10
14. 1
15. 9
16. 5
17. 2
18. 8
19. 6
20. 4

A rapid recall session:

1. 3 × 2
2. 7 × 2
3. 4 × 2
4. 1 × 2
5. 6 × 2
6. 10 × 2
7. 2 × 2
8. 9 × 2
9. 5 × 2
10. 8 × 2

11. How many twos make 6?
12. How many twos make 14?
13. How many twos make 20?
14. How many twos make 2?
15. How many twos make 18?
16. How many twos make 10?
17. How many twos make 4?
18. How many twos make 16?
19. How many twos make 12?
20. How many twos make 8?

What's the problem?

Learning objective Represent the information in a puzzle or problem using numbers, images or diagrams; use these to find a solution and present it in context, where appropriate using £.p notation or units of measure. **Type of starter** Reason **Mental strategy** Encourage children to use mental strategies to work out the answer to each problem and then to use the number line to support their answers.	**Resources** A board or flipchart

Write the following calculations on the board:

1. ☐ - 35 = 20   20 - ☐ = 35

   ☐ - 20 = 35   35 - ☐ = 20

Answers
1.   35 - 15 = 20
2.   22 + 18 = 40

Now read the following problem to the class:

Joe had 35 computer games. He sold some of them to his friend and had 20 left.

Ask the class first to write the number of games that Joe sold; then to identify which is the correct number sentence on the board. Point to each one in turn and ask the children to vote for what they think is the correct sentence.

Repeat for the following problem:

Sam has 22 football stickers. There are 40 stickers in the full set. How many more stickers does he need?

2.   40 + ☐ = 22   22 + ☐ = 40

   22 + 40 = ☐

Repeat with other similar examples. After each answer, ask someone to come to the board to show how they worked out the answer using an empty number line, for example:

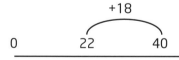

BLOCK B

③⓪ **Addition grid**

Resources	**Learning objective**
Incomplete addition grid drawn on the board; paper and pencils for each pair	Identify patterns and relationships involving numbers or shapes, and use these to solve problems.
	Type of starter
	Refine

Answers

Nine sets of four statements (see example left).

Divide the class into mixed-ability pairs. Discuss the grid below briefly, asking where would be a good place to start. Ask individuals to fill the empty cells and (if possible) to explain how they reached the answers.

Solve one-step and two-step problems involving numbers, money or measures, including time, choosing and carrying out appropriate calculations.

When the grid is complete, ask the children to work in pairs, writing as many addition and subtraction statements from the grid as they can. Write examples on the board:

2 + 6 = 8   6 + 2 = 8

8 - 2 = 6   8 - 6 = 2

+	2		7
6		9	
7			
			19

▲SCHOLASTIC

Imagine this shape

<table>
<tr><td>

Learning objective
Relate 2D shapes and 3D solids to drawings of them; describe, visualise, classify, draw and make the shapes.

Type of starter
Read

Mental strategy
Encourage the children to imagine the shapes. For less confident learners, provide sets of 2D and 3D shapes.

</td><td>

Resources
A board or flipchart

</td></tr>
</table>

On the board write the first property of the shape that you are thinking of. Read the property together. Ask the children what they think the shape is. Ask: *Can we be sure with just this information?* Now give more information so that the children can work out what the shape is. For example:

1. *I am thinking of a shape which has six faces. All the faces are the same shape. All the faces are the same size.*

Repeat this for other shapes. For example:

2. *My shape has more than six sides. My shape has a line of symmetry.*

3. *My shape has a square base. It has four more faces. Each of these faces are triangular.*

Answers

1. Cube
2. Octagon (some children will know heptagon, nonagon and so on)
3. Pyramid, square-based

 Lines of symmetry

<table>
<tr><td>

Learning objective
Draw and complete shapes with reflective symmetry; draw the reflection of a shape in a mirror line along one side.

Type of starter
Reason

</td><td>

Resources
A whiteboard

</td></tr>
</table>

Ask the children to think of a shape that you say. Then invite them, in their heads, to draw a line of symmetry through the shape and say which shapes are formed. Draw with the children and discuss alternative lines of symmetry and shapes formed where appropriate.

No set answers

BLOCK B

(33) **Number fractions**

Resources	Learning objective
A board or flipchart; one copy of 'Number fractions' (from photocopiable page 91) per child; coloured pencils	Read and write proper fractions (eg 3/7, 9/10), interpreting the denominator as the parts of a whole and the numerator as the number of parts; identify and estimate fractions of shapes; use diagrams to compare fractions and establish equivalents. **Type of starter** Refine

No set answers

Draw a rectangle divided into quarters.

Ask a child to shade in one quarter of the rectangle. Now, shade another quarter.

Ask: *What fraction of the rectangle is shaded?* Establish that: two quarters equal one half, $^1/_4 + {}^1/_4 = {}^1/_2$. Repeat for the other shape fractions on photocopiable page 91.

(34) **Half and quarter**

Resources	Learning objective
A board or flipchart	Read and write proper fractions (eg 3/7, 9/10), interpreting the denominator as the parts of a whole and the numerator as the number of parts. **Type of starter** Refresh

Answers

1. 5
2. 50
3. 3
4. 12
5. 2
6. 5
7. 1
8. 3

Remind the children that to find a half, we divide by 2.

Write: $^1/_4$ of $12 = 12 \div 4 = 3$ or $12 \rightarrow 6 \rightarrow 3$. Stress that to find a quarter we divide by 4 or we halve twice.

What is half of:

1.	10	3.	6
2.	100	4.	24

What is one quarter of:

5.	8	7.	4
6.	20	8.	12

(35) Money puzzles

Learning objective	Resources
Represent the information in a puzzle or problem using numbers, images or diagrams; use these to find a solution and present it in context, where appropriate using £.p notation or units of measure. **Type of starter** Reason	'Money puzzles' (from photocopiable page 92)

Copy and display the photocopiable page on OHT or give each child a copy.

Write in three amounts on the board. For example:

1.   6p + 7p + 5p = ____

Ask the children to write the answer on their whiteboards, then to hold them up when you say 'Show me!'

Tell each group that they have three coins. Each coin is worth more than 5p. Ask them to come up with three different totals using different combinations of coins.

Give the groups five minutes to prepare their number sentences, then ask a member from each group to read each number sentence – starting with their smallest total and finishing with the largest total.

You might want to keep a supply of real coins to check the children's answers with the whole class.

Answers
1.   18p

(36) Mental subtraction

Learning objective	Resources
Derive and recall all addition and subtraction facts for each number to 20, sums and differences of multiples of 10 and number pairs that total 100. **Type of starter** Reason	A board or flipchart

Write: 34 – 18 = and 42 – 28 =.

Allow the children a minute to work out the answers.

Discuss the methods used. Gather (or if necessary, suggest) methods such as: using the nearest 'tens' number and then adjusting; using a near double.

Write the following and discuss methods:

1.   39 – 19 =   3.   34 – 18 =

2.   46 – 23 =   4.   42 – 29 =

Answers
1.   20
2.   23
3.   16
4.   13

BLOCK B

 Table talk

Resources	**Learning objective**
None	Derive and recall multiplication facts for the two-, three-, four-, five-, six- and ten-times tables and the corresponding division facts; recognise multiples of 2, 5 or 10 up to 1000.
	Type of starter
	Recall

Answers

1. 10
2. 14
3. 80
4. 12
5. 45
6. 25
7. 18
8. 60
9. 35
10. 5
11. 12
12. 16
13. 50
14. 30
15. 70
16. 20
17. 8
18. 30
19. 12
20. 40

Address questions to individuals:

1. 2 × 5
2. 7 × 2
3. 8 × 10
4. 6 × 2
5. 9 × 5
6. 5 × 5
7. 9 × 2
8. 6 × 10
9. 7 × 5
10. 1 × 5

11. 4 × 3
12. 8 × 2
13. 5 × 10
14. 6 × 5
15. 7 × 10
16. 5 × 4
17. 4 × 2
18. 10 × 3
19. 3 × 4
20. 8 × 5

Doubles

Learning objective	Resources
Use knowledge of number operations and corresponding inverses, including doubling and halving, to estimate and check calculations. **Type of starter** Recall	The numbers 0-10 (inclusive) written on a board or OHT, well spaced and at child height

Ask for a volunteer to write the double of any number (0-10) beneath that number on the board or OHT. Continue until they are all done (each volunteer writes one answer).

Ask questions 1-10 while the class can see the answers.

Gradually erase the better-known doubles while repeating questions 1-10.

Erase all the doubles and ask questions 11-20, with the children raising their hands to answer individually.

1.	double 3	11.	2 times 5
2.	double 8	12.	add 3 to itself
3.	double 5	13.	twice 8
4.	double 1	14.	double 1
5.	double 7	15.	add 7 to 7
6.	double 0	16.	2 times 10
7.	double 4	17.	double 6
8.	double 9	18.	add 9 to itself
9.	double 2	19.	twice 2
10.	double 6	20.	double 0

Answers
1. 6
2. 16
3. 10
4. 2
5. 14
6. 0
7. 8
8. 18
9. 4
10. 12
11. 10
12. 6
13. 16
14. 2
15. 14
16. 20
17. 12
18. 18
19. 4
20. 0

BLOCK B

(39) **Shape fractions**

Resources A board or flipchart; one copy of 'Shape fractions' (from photocopiable page 93) per child; coloured pencils	**Learning objective** Identify and estimate fractions of shapes; use diagrams to compare fractions and establish equivalents. **Type of starter** Refresh **Mental strategy** Draw three aligned rectangles and divide them into halves, quarters and eighths respectively to highlight the equivalence.
No set answers	Write some examples of equivalent fractions. For example: $^1/_4 + {}^1/_4 = {}^2/_4 = {}^1/_2$ $^1/_8 + {}^1/_8 = {}^2/_8 = {}^1/_4$ $^1/_8 + {}^1/_8 + {}^1/_8 + {}^1/_8 = {}^4/_8 = {}^2/_4 = {}^1/_2$ Provide the children with a copy of the photocopiable page to complete. Allow a short time for the children to complete the sheet, then ask them for some equivalent fractions. List these on the board. Include $^3/_4$ and its equivalents if offered.

(40) **Twice as much**

Resources None	**Learning objective** Solve one-step and two-step problems involving numbers, money or measures, including time, choosing and carrying out appropriate calculations. **Type of starter** Rehearse
Answers 1. 17 2. 20 3. 30 4. 29 5. 17 6. 3 7. 22 8. 20	Recap known doubles and halves, then ask the following questions: 1. Double 6 plus 5 2. Double 13 minus 6 3. Double 5 times 3 4. Double 16 minus 3 5. Half of 22 plus 6 6. Half of 16 minus 5 7. Half of 38 plus 3 8. Half of 10 times 4

(41) Matchstick shapes

Learning objective
Relate 2D shapes and 3D solids to drawings of them; describe, visualise, classify, draw and make the shapes.

Type of starter
Recall

Mental strategy
The children will need to recall the shapes mentally in order to be able to make them. Encourage those who are unsure to 'see' the shape in their heads before they begin to make it.

Resources
12 matchsticks or thin sticks of uniform size for each child

Explain that you will say the name of a 2D shape. Ask the children to use their matchsticks to make the shape. Ask them to compare their shape with their neighbour and to discuss any differences between their shapes. Say:

1. Make a square.
   How many sticks did you use?
   How many sides does a square have?
   What type of angles does it have?

2. Make a rectangle.
   How many sticks did you use?
   What can you tell me about opposite sides?

3. Make a triangle.
   How many sticks did you use?
   Make a different triangle. How many sticks did you use this time?

4. Make a pentagon.
   How many sticks did you use?
   Make a different pentagon. How many sticks did you use this time?

5. Make a hexagon.
   How many sticks did you use?
   Make a different hexagon. How many sticks did you use this time?

6. Make an octagon.
   How many sticks did you use?
   How many vertices does an octagon have?

7. Make a quadrilateral.
   How many sides does a quadrilateral have?
   Make a different quadrilateral? How is it different?

Answers
1. 4 sides; 4 right angles.

2. Opposite sides equal in length and parallel.

3-5. N/A

6. 8 vertices

7. Check that the children make different quadrilaterals and do not just enlarge the first one by adding more sticks to each side.

BLOCK B

(42) Properties of 2D shapes

Resources
Individual whiteboards and pens

Learning objective
Identify patterns and relationships involving numbers or shapes and use these to solve problems.

Type of starter
Read

Answers

1. Triangle: 3 straight sides; 3 angles.

2. Square: 4 straight sides; 4 right angles; all sides are the same length.

3. Rectangle: 4 straight sides; 4 right angles; opposite sides are the same length.

4. Pentagon: 5 straight sides; 5 angles.

5. Octagon: 8 straight sides; 8 angles.

6. Hexagon: 6 straight sides; 6 angles.

7. Circle: 1 curved side which is continuous.

Explain that you will write the name of a shape on the board. Ask the children to draw the shape on their whiteboard. Then, when you say 'show me', they should hold up their whiteboards for you to check. Write:

1. Triangle

2. Square

3. Rectangle

4. Pentagon

5. Octagon

6. Hexagon

7. Circle

Now ask the children to put their whiteboards down. Explain that you will point to a shape name on the board. Ask the children to put up their hands to tell you a property that the shape has.

BLOCK C

Unit 1

Page	Objective	Activity title	Starter type	Unit	Lesson	Page
	100 Mental Maths Starters			**100 Maths Lessons**		
43	Know the relationships between kilometres and metres, metres and centimetres, kilograms and grams, litres and millilitres; choose and use appropriate units to estimate, measure and record measurements.	43 Measuring units	Recall	1	1	97
44	Read, to the nearest division and half-division, scales that are numbered or partially numbered; use the information to measure and draw to a suitable degree of accuracy.	44 Centimetre number line	Read	1	3	98
45	Know the relationships between kilometres and metres, metres and centimetres, kilograms and grams, litres and millilitres; choose and use appropriate units to estimate, measure and record measurements.	45 Metric facts	Recall	1	4	99
46	Use Venn diagrams or Carroll diagrams to sort data and objects using more than one criterion.	46 Sort and sort again	Reason	1	6	101
47	Use Venn diagrams or Carroll diagrams to sort data and objects using more than one criterion.	47 Carroll diagrams	Reason	1	7 or 8	101/102
47	Answer a question by collecting, organising and interpreting data; use tally charts, frequency tables, pictograms and bar charts to represent results and illustrate observations; use ICT to create a simple bar chart.	48 Tally chart	Rehearse	1	9	103

Unit 2

Page	Objective	Activity title	Starter type	Unit	Lesson	Page
	100 Mental Maths Starters			**100 Maths Lessons**		
48	Know the relationships between kilometres and metres, metres and centimetres, kilograms and grams, litres and millilitres; choose and use appropriate units to estimate, measure and record measurements.	49 Which units?	Reason	2	1	107
48	Read, to the nearest division and half-division, scales that are numbered or partially numbered; use the information to measure and draw to a suitable degree of accuracy.	50 Centimetre competition	Reason	2	2	108
49	Read the time on a 12-hour digital clock and to the nearest 5 minutes on an analogue clock; calculate time intervals and find start or end times for a given time interval.	51 Any time	Rehearse	2	4	109

Unit 2 ...continued

100 Mental Maths Starters				100 Maths Lessons		
Page	Objective	Activity title	Starter type	Unit	Lesson	Page
49	Read the time on a 12-hour digital clock and to the nearest 5 minutes on an analogue clock; calculate time intervals and find start or end times for a given time interval.	52 5 minutes later	Rehearse	2	5	110
50	Answer a question by collecting, organising and interpreting data; use tally charts, frequency tables, pictograms and bar charts to represent results and illustrate observations; use ICT to create a simple bar chart.	53 Reading a pictogram	Refine	2	7, 8, or 9	112-115
51	Use Venn diagrams or Carroll diagrams to sort data and objects using more than one criterion.	54 Playing card sort	Rehearse	2	10	116

Unit 3

100 Mental Maths Starters				100 Maths Lessons		
Page	Objective	Activity title	Starter type	Unit	Lesson	Page
52	Know the relationships between kilometres and metres, metres and centimetres, kilograms and grams, litres and millilitres; choose and use appropriate units to estimate, measure and record measurements.	55 Converting metric units	Reason	3	1	121
52	Know the relationships between kilometres and metres, metres and centimetres, kilograms and grams, litres and millilitres; choose and use appropriate units to estimate, measure and record measurements.	56 Estimating measurements	Reason	3	2	120
53	Know the relationships between litres and millilitres; choose and use appropriate units to estimate, measure and record measurements.	57 Capacity	Rehearse	3	3	122
53	Read, to the nearest division and half-division, scales that are numbered or partially numbered; use the information to measure and draw to a suitable degree of accuracy.	58 Using a ruler	Read	3	4	122
54	Read, to the nearest division and half-division, scales that are numbered or partially numbered; use the information to measure and draw to a suitable degree of accuracy.	59 Estimate and measure competition	Read	3	5	122
54	Answer a question by collecting, organising and interpreting data; use tally charts, frequency tables, pictograms and bar charts to represent results and illustrate observations; use ICT to create a simple bar chart.	60 Favourite sports	Read	3	10	126

(43) Measuring units

Learning objective
Know the relationships between kilometres and metres, metres and centimetres, kilograms and grams, litres and millilitres; choose and use appropriate units to estimate, measure and record measurements.

Type of starter
Recall

Mental strategy
This activity is about recalling facts about metric measures. If children are unsure ask them to shut their eyes and imagine each unit's size so that they can compare them.

Resources
A board or flipchart

Explain that you will ask some questions about measuring units. Say:

1. Which is larger, a gram or a kilogram?

2. Which is the smaller unit, a metre or a centimetre?

3. Which is the larger unit, a millilitre or a litre?

4. How many centimetres are there in a metre?

5. How many 100ml make a litre?

6. How many 200g do you need to make a kilogram?

7. How many metres make a kilometre?

8. If I walk 3 kilometres how many metres would that be?

Answers
1. Kilogram
2. Centimetre
3. Litre
4. 100
5. 10
6. 5
7. 1000
8. 3000

BLOCK C

⁴⁴ Centimetre number line

Resources
Number line drawn on the board, marked into ten divisions

Learning objective
Read, to the nearest division and half-division, scales that are numbered or partially numbered; use the information to measure and draw to a suitable degree of accuracy.

Type of starter
Read

Mental strategy
Encourage the children to use their mental image of a number line to complete this activity.

No set answers

Label one end of the number line 0cm and the other end 10cm. Say a measure in centimetres and then invite a child to come to the board and point to the relevant position on the line. Write the value onto the line. Say, for example:

1. Where would 5cm fit?

2. Where would 9cm be?

Now clear the values, and write 0cm and 100cm at the ends of the line. Repeat the activity using tens, such as:

3. Where would 30cm fit?

4. Where is 80cm?

5. Where do you think 75cm would be?

Clear the board again. Write 20cm one end of the line and 30cm the other. Point to positions on the line and ask the children to tell you what number they think would be there. Repeat, filling in the numbers along the line.

(45) Metric facts

Learning objective
Know the relationships between kilometres and metres, metres and centimetres, kilograms and grams, litres and millilitres; choose and use appropriate units to estimate, measure and record measurements.

Resources
Individual whiteboards and pens

Type of starter
Recall

Mental strategy
If children are unsure about these facts, provide some measuring devices so that they can examine these and read the scales.

Ask the children to write their answers on their whiteboards. When you say 'show me', they should hold up their boards for you to see. Say:

1. How many centimetres are there in a metre?

2. How many metres are there in a kilometre?

3. How many millilitres are there in a litre?

4. How many grams are there in a kilogram?

5. How many centimetres are there in half a metre?

6. How many centimetres are there in a quarter of a metre?

7. How many millilitres are there in half a litre?

8. How many grams are there in half a kilogram?

9. How many millilitres are there in a quarter of a litre?

10. How many grams are there in 2 kilograms?

Answers
1. 100
2. 1000
3. 1000
4. 1000
5. 50
6. 25
7. 500
8. 500
9. 250
10. 2000

(46) Sort and sort again

Resources
Data collection charts displayed for the whole class. (Keep the completed charts for the next activity.)

Learning objective
Use Venn diagrams or Carroll diagrams to sort data and objects using more than one criterion.

Type of starter
Reason

Mental strategy
Children may find it helpful to think of these numbers on a number line in their heads.

Answers

1. Odd: 251, 253, 255, 257, 259, 261, 263, 265, 267, 269, 271, 273, 275, 277, 279, 281, 283, 285, 287, 289, 291, 293, 295, 297, 299.

    Even: 250, 252, 254, 256, 258, 260, 262, 264, 266, 268, 270, 272, 274, 276, 278, 280, 282, 284, 286, 288, 290, 292, 294, 296, 298, 300.

2. Divisible by 10 with no remainder: 250, 260, 270, 280, 290, 300. The rest do not divide by 10 with no remainder.

3. Those with 9 in their unit's place: 259, 269, 279, 289, 299.

4. Children will suggest many different ways of sorting these numbers.

Create a data collection chart and display this to the class (The headings will be different for each instruction.)

Numbers 250 to 300

Odd numbers	Even numbers

Ask the children to help you to sort the numbers 250 to 300. Say:

1. Sort the numbers into odd and even.

2. Now sort the numbers into those that can be divided with no remainder by 10 and those that cannot.

3. Sort again: numbers that have a 9 in their units place and those that do not.

4. Now suggest another way that these numbers can be sorted.

Carroll diagrams

Learning objective	Resources
Use Venn diagrams or Carroll diagrams to sort data and objects using more than one criterion. **Type of starter** Reason	Carroll diagrams displayed for the whole class; the data charts from the previous activity

Explain that you would like the children to help you to transfer the data collected yesterday onto some Carroll diagrams. For odd and even numbers ask:

1. What title shall we use?
2. What heading goes in the first column?
3. What heading goes in the second column?

Repeat this for the other data collection charts.

Now ask the children to sort the numbers 320 to 370 into those that can be divided exactly by 5 and those that cannot. Ask them to draw a Carroll diagram and write their own headings.

Answers
1. Odd and even numbers, for example.
2. Odd numbers or Even numbers.
3. Not odd numbers or Not even numbers.

 Tally chart

Learning objective	Resources
Answer a question by collecting, organising and interpreting data; use tally charts, frequency tables, pictograms and bar charts to represent results and illustrate observations; use ICT to create a simple bar chart. **Type of starter** Rehearse **Mental strategy** In order to count up tallies children need to be able to count accurately in fives. For those who find this difficult, practise counting in fives together from zero.	A simple data collection chart displayed for the whole class; a simple data collection chart for each group

Show the children the data collection chart. Explain that you would like them to collect some data from their group. This will then go onto the class data collection chart. Ask:

1. Find out how many brothers and sisters there are for your group.

When the children have collected the data, discuss how they collected it.

Now combine the data onto the class data collection chart using tally marks for each group's data. Ask:

2. How can we count up the tally marks quickly?

Invite the children to count with you in fives, then count on any ones that are left to make the total.

Repeat for another data collection (eg favourite crisp flavours), this time asking the children to use tally marks on their data collection chart. Combine the charts afterwards to make a class chart.

Answers
1. N/A
2. Count in fives.

(49) **Which units?**

Resources
A selection of classroom resources providing different measures, weights and capacities

Learning objective
Know the relationships between kilometres and metres, metres and centimetres, kilograms and grams, litres and millilitres; choose and use appropriate units to estimate, measure and record measurements.

Type of starter
Reason

Mental strategy
Ask the children to explain how they made their decision. In doing this they are using the knowledge they have to reason out which units would be most suitable.

Answers

1. Centimetres
2. Centimetres or metres depending on length.
3. Grams or kilograms depending on weight.
6. Millilitres
7. Litres

Explain that you have some items for the children to investigate. Ask them to think about what units they would choose to measure them. For example:

1. What unit would you choose to measure the length of this pencil?
2. What unit would you choose to measure the length of this stick?
3. What unit would you choose to find out how heavy this parcel is? (Pass the parcel around so that the children can feel its weight.)
6. What unit would you use to find out how much this cup holds?
7. What unit would you choose to find out how much this bottle holds?

(50) **Centimetre competition**

Resources
Rulers marked in centimetres and half centimetres; paper, pencils

Learning objective
Read, to the nearest division and half-division, scales that are numbered or partially numbered; use the information to measure and draw to a suitable degree of accuracy.

Type of starter
Reason

Mental strategy
Encourage the children to compare their estimated line with the line that they draw to the correct length, then use this to reason out their next estimate.

No set answers

In pairs, ask the children to estimate and draw a line to the length that you say. Then ask them to swap papers to measure the line with a ruler and write its length. The one who is closest to the measure gets a point. Say:

1. Draw a line that is 10cm long.
2. Draw a line that is 8cm long.
3. Draw a line that is 4cm long.
4. Draw a line that is 11cm long.
5. Draw a line that is 6cm long.

This can be repeated with measurements between 2cm and 11cm.

BLOCK C

(51) Any time

Learning objective	Resources
Read the time on a 12-hour digital clock and to the nearest 5 minutes on an analogue clock; calculate time intervals and find start or end times for a given time interval. **Type of starter** Rehearse	A teaching clock; one clock face between two children

Move the minute hand from the o'clock position, saying the time together every 5 minutes (eg '5 minutes past'... , '25 minutes to'...) all the way round.

No set answers

Ask the children to show and say these times on their clock faces:

1. 10 o'clock
2. 10 minutes past 10
3. 20 minutes past 10
4. 5 minutes past 10
5. 15 minutes past 10

6. 30 minutes past 10
7. 5 minutes to 11
8. 25 minutes to 11
9. 10 minutes to 11
10. 20 minutes to 11

Repeat, starting at 6 o'clock.

(52) 5 minutes later

Learning objective	Resources
Read the time on a 12-hour digital clock and to the nearest 5 minutes on an analogue clock; calculate time intervals and find start or end times for a given time interval. **Type of starter** Rehearse	A teaching clock; one clock face between two children

Ask the children to take turns (within each pair) to show the times that you say:

No set answers

1. 10 minutes past 9
2. 20 minutes past 12
3. 25 minutes past 7
4. 5 minutes past 11
5. quarter past 6

6. half past 8
7. 5 minutes to 4
8. 25 minutes to 1
9. 20 minutes to 5
10. 10 minutes to 3

Repeat, asking the children to advance each time by five minutes and say the new time.

(53) **Reading a pictogram**

Resources
One copy of 'Car colour pictogram' enlarged to A3 (from photocopiable page 94) per child

Learning objective
Answer a question by collecting, organising and interpreting data; use tally charts, frequency tables, pictograms and bar charts to represent results and illustrate observations; use ICT to create a simple bar chart.

Type of starter
Refine

Mental strategy
Children will need to use their knowledge of the four-times table. If they are unsure, count together in fours.

Answers

1. 4
2. 2
3. 1
4. 18
5. 10
6. 9
7. Silver
8. Green
9. 3
10. 8

Ask the children to look carefully at the pictogram. Ask:

1. How many cars does the circle represent?

2. How many cars does the half circle represent?

3. How many cars does the quarter circle represent?

4. How many of the cars are red?

5. How many of the cars are black?

6. How many of the cars are green?

7. Which is the most popular colour of car?

8. Which is the least popular colour of car?

9. How many more silver cars are there than red ones?

10. How many fewer black cars are there than red ones?

(54) Playing card sort

Learning objective
Use Venn diagrams or Carroll diagrams to sort data and objects using more than one criterion.

Type of starter
Rehearse

Mental strategy
Children need to understand the meaning of 'not' in the Carroll diagram. So, if they pick a black card with no picture it goes in the Not red column in the Not picture card row.

Resources
A pack of playing cards; Blue-Tack®; a Carroll diagram displayed for the whole class

Answers
1. Red card column.
2. Not red card column.
3. Yes. It must go in the Picture card row.
4. First quadrant or first column, first row.

Display the following Carroll diagram:

Playing card sort

	Red card	Not red card
Picture card		
Not picture card		

Give everybody in the class a playing card. Invite the children to come out, one by one, and decide where to place their card on the diagram, fixing it with Blue-Tack. The other children check that they agree with the placement of the card.

When all the children have placed their cards, ask:

1. Where do the red cards go?

2. So where do the black cards go?

3. Does it matter if a card has a picture?

4. Where would a red card with a picture go?

BLOCK C

(55) Converting metric units

Resources
Individual whiteboards and pens

Learning objective
Know the relationships between kilometres and metres, metres and centimetres, kilograms and grams, litres and millilitres; choose and use appropriate units to estimate, measure and record measurements.

Type of starter
Reason

Mental strategy
If children are unsure, discuss how 100g or 100ml is ¹/₁₀ of a kilogram or litre and that this is the same as 0.1kg or 0.1l. Then discuss 200g and so on. Children can plot these values on an empty number line to help them.

Answers
1. 0.5m
2. 0.5kg
3. 0.25l
4. 0.2kg
5. 1.5m
6. 0.75l

Explain to the children that they are going to convert different units of measure. Ask them to write the answers on their whiteboards and when you say 'show me', they are to hold these up for you to see. Say, for example:

1. A piece of string is 50cm long. Write this in metres.
2. A can of beans weighs 500g. Write this in kilograms.
3. A glass holds 250ml. Write this in litres.
4. A bag of toffees weighs 200g. Write this in kilograms.
5. Tom's height is 150cm. How would you write this in metres?
6. The bottle of orange has 750ml left. Write this in litres.

(56) Estimating measurements

Resources
Cups and bottles of varying capacities; parcels of varying weights and sizes; a litre measuring jug; a ruler marked in centimetres and half centimetres; a balance with 100g and 1kg masses

Learning objective
Know the relationships between kilometres and metres, metres and centimetres, kilograms and grams, litres and millilitres; choose and use appropriate units to estimate, measure and record measurements.

Type of starter
Reason

Mental strategy
Encourage the children to make estimates based on previous experience.

No set answers

Ask the children to estimate a series of measures. Once they have made each estimate, ask a child to measure the item as accurately as they can.

Compare the estimates with the final measure so that children have the opportunity to improve their estimating skills. Ask:

1. How much do you think this cup will hold?
2. How heavy do you think this parcel is?
3. How long do you estimate this table to be?
4. How much do you think this bottle will hold?

Capacity

Learning objective Know the relationships between litres and millilitres; choose and use appropriate units to estimate, measure and record measurments **Type of starter** Rehearse **Mental strategy** Children may find a mental number line helpful to count along and back in hundreds, 500s, or whole and part litres.	**Resources** Individual whiteboards and pens

Read the following questions with a pause between each one. When the final sentence has been read and the children have written their answers, invite them to hold up their boards for you to see. Ask:

1. The bottle holds 1 litre. I pour out 600ml. Then I pour back 200ml. How much is in the bottle now?

2. The large bottle holds 4 litres. I pour out 2¹/₂ litres. I pour out another ¹/₂ litre. Now I pour 500ml into the bottle. How much is in the bottle now?

3. 5 children want a drink of water. The bottle holds 1¹/₂ litres of water. How much water does each child receive if the bottle is emptied?

Answers
1. 600ml
2. 1.5l or 1¹/₂ litres or 1500ml
3. 300ml

58 Using a ruler

Learning objective Read, to the nearest division and half-division, scales that are numbered or partially numbered; use the information to measure and draw to a suitable degree of accuracy. **Type of starter** Read	**Resources** A ruler for each child marked in centimetres and half centimetres

Ask the children to show the following measurements on their rulers:

1. 5cm; 9¹/₂ cm;15cm
2. The measurement halfway between 16cm and 19cm.
3. The measurement that is halfway between 12cm and 17cm.

Now ask the children to use the ruler to draw the lines that you say. They can check each other's lines by measuring them. Say:

4. Draw a line that is 8cm long. Now draw a line that is 4¹/₂ cm long.
5. Draw a line that is longer than 8cm. Write its measurement.
6. Draw a line that is shorter than 6cm. Write its measurement.
7. Draw a line that is between 7¹/₂ cm and 9¹/₂ cm. Write its measurement.

Answers
2. 17¹/₂ cm
3. 14¹/₂ cm

BLOCK C

59 Estimate and measure competition

Resources
One copy 'Estimate and measure' (see photocopiable page 95) per child; a ruler for each child marked in centimetres and half centimetres

Learning objective
Read, to the nearest division and half-division, scales that are numbered or partially numbered; use the information to measure and draw to a suitable degree of accuracy.

Type of starter
Read

Mental strategy
Children should use what they learn from the first line to improve their estimate for the next, and so on.

No set answers

Give each child a copy of photocopiable page 95. Explain that they should estimate the length of each line first and then measure it. They then record their estimate, measure, and the difference between the two in the spaces provided. The difference between the estimate and the measure is their score.

60 Favourite sports

Resources
A bar chart on screen or on paper

Learning objective
Answer a question by collecting, organising and interpreting data; use tally charts, frequency tables, pictograms and bar charts to represent results and illustrate observations; use ICT to create a simple bar chart.

Type of starter
Read

Mental strategy
Children need to be able to count on in the chosen scale. Rehearse this if they are unsure.

Answers

Answers will depend upon the data collected.

Ask the children to work in groups to collect data about their favourite sports. From this make a class data collection chart. Discuss what the scale should be (eg 1, 2, 5 or 10). When the bar chart is completed ask:

1. How many people chose...? How did you work that out?

2. Which is the most popular sport? How many people chose that?

3. Which is the least popular sport? How many people chose that?

4. Which sport is more popular than...?

5. How many more people liked... than...?

6. How many fewer people liked... than...?

BLOCK D

Unit 1

100 Mental Maths Starters				100 Maths Lessons		
Page	Objective	Activity title	Starter type	Unit	Lesson	Page
57	Solve one-step and two-step problems involving numbers, money or measures, including time, choosing and carrying out appropriate calculations.	**61** Hundred square	Refine	1	1	131
57	Add or subtract mentally combinations of one-digit and two-digit numbers.	**62** Cross the bridge	Refine	1	2	132
58	Find unit fractions of numbers and quantities (eg $1/2$, $1/3$, $1/4$ and $1/6$ of 12 litres).	**63** Fractions of a metre	Rehearse	1	4	134
59	Read and record the vocabulary of position, direction and movement, using the four compass directions to describe movement about a grid.	**64** Coordinates	Refresh	1	8	137
60	Read, to the nearest division and half-division, scales that are numbered or partially numbered; use the information to measure and draw to a suitable degree of accuracy.	**65** Drawing and measuring lines	Refine	1	9	137
61	Know the relationships between kilometres and metres, metres and centimetres, kilograms and grams, litres and millilitres; choose and use appropriate units to estimate, measure and record measurements.	**66** Cake making	Rehearse	1	10	138

Unit 2

100 Mental Maths Starters				100 Maths Lessons		
Page	Objective	Activity title	Starter type	Unit	Lesson	Page
62	Add or subtract mentally combinations of one-digit and two-digit numbers.	**67** Target totals	Rehearse	2	1	144
63	Develop and use written methods to record, support or explain addition and subtraction of two-digit and three-digit numbers.	**68** Shoe shop add and subtract	Refine	2	3	145
64	Use practical and informal written methods to multiply and divide two-digit numbers (eg 13×3, $50 \div 4$); round remainders up or down, depending on the context.	**69** Multiplication and division	Reason	2	4	145
65	Find unit fractions of numbers and quantities (eg $1/2$, $1/3$, $1/4$ and $1/6$ of 12 litres).	**70** Pieces of 8	Refresh	2	5	146

Unit 2 ...continued

	100 Mental Maths Starters			100 Maths Lessons		
Page	Objective	Activity title	Starter type	Unit	Lesson	Page
66	Draw and complete shapes with reflective symmetry; draw the reflection of a shape in a mirror line along one side.	(71) Reflections	Read	2	6	147
67	Represent the information in a puzzle or problem using numbers, images or diagrams; use these to find a solution and present it in context, where appropriate using £.p notation or units of measure.	(72) Choose the numbers calculations	Reason	2	10	149

Unit 3

	100 Mental Maths Starters			100 Maths Lessons		
Page	Objective	Activity title	Starter type	Unit	Lesson	Page
67	Use knowledge of number operations and corresponding inverses, including doubling and halving, to estimate and check calculations.	(73) Addition and subtraction facts	Refine	3	1	157
68	Develop and use written methods to record, support or explain addition and subtraction of two-digit and three-digit numbers.	(74) Number sentences	Reason	3	4	159
68	Use practical and informal written methods to multiply and divide two-digit numbers (eg 13 × 3, 50 ÷ 4); round remainders up or down, depending on the context.	(75) Tens	Refine	3	5	159
69	Understand that division is the inverse of multiplication and vice versa; use this to derive and record related multiplication and division number sentences.	(76) Right shift	Refresh	3	6	160
69	Read, to the nearest division and half-division, scales that are numbered or partially numbered; use the information to measure and draw to a suitable degree of accuracy.	(77) Reading grams	Read	3	9	162
70	Read the time on a 12-hour digital clock and to the nearest 5 minutes on an analogue clock; calculate time intervals and find start or end times for a given time interval.	(78) Take five	Rehearse	3	10	163

(61) Hundred square

Learning objective
Solve one-step and two-step problems involving numbers, money or measures, including time, choosing and carrying out appropriate calculations.

Type of starter
Refine

Mental strategy
Ask the children to take 86 from 100

Show them two ways to move from 86 to 100 on the 1-100 square: move across to 90 and then down to 100 or move down to 96 and then across to 100.

Resources
'1-100 square' (enlarged from photocopiable page 90)

Ask the children to use the 1-100 square to answer the following:

1.	100 – 88	6.	100 – 66
2.	100 – 81	7.	100 – 52
3.	100 – 77	8.	100 – 50
4.	100 – 74	9.	100 – 37
5.	100 – 68	10.	100 – 63

Answers

1.	12	6.	34
2.	19	7.	48
3.	23	8.	50
4.	26	9.	63
5.	32	10.	37

(62) Cross the bridge

Learning objective
Add or subtract mentally combinations of one-digit and two-digit numbers.

Type of starter
Refine

Mental strategy
Demonstrate 6 + 7 on the board, partitioning 7 into 4 + 3 so the 4 can be added first.

Resources
A board or flipchart

Practise adding numbers to 10 to build the children's confidence.

1.	10 + 8	7.	8 + 6
2.	10 + 4	8.	7 + 5
3.	10 + 3	9.	6 + 9
4.	10 + 5	10.	9 + 5
5.	10 + 0	11.	6 + 6
6.	10 + 2	12.	8 + 3

Answers

1.	18	7.	14
2.	14	8.	12
3.	13	9.	15
4.	15	10.	14
5.	10	11.	12
6.	12	12.	11

BLOCK D

(63) **Fractions of a metre**

Resources
A metre rule marked in centimetres; rulers for the children marked in centimetres to 30cm

Learning objective
Find unit fractions of numbers and quantities (eg $^1/_2$, $^1/_3$, $^1/_4$ and $^1/_6$ of 12 litres).

Type of starter
Rehearse

Mental strategy
Encourage the children to work mentally to answer the problems, using table facts for division.

Answers

1. $^1/_2$
2. $^1/_4$
3. $^3/_4$
4. 15cm
5. 6cm
6. 3cm
7. 10cm
8. 5cm
9. 20kg
10. 10kg
11. 8kg
12. 6kg

Point to a mark on the metre rule and ask the children what fraction it is of a metre. For example:

1. Point to 50cm.

2. Point to 25cm.

3. Point to 75cm.

Next, ask the children to find and show the following on their rulers:

4. Half of 30cm

5. $^1/_5$ of 30cm

6. $^1/_{10}$ of 30cm

7. $^1/_3$ of 30cm

8. $^1/_6$ of 30cm

Now ask the children to answer these problems:

9. What is half of 40kg?

10. What is a quarter of 40kg?

11. What is a fifth of 40kg?

12. What is a sixth of 36kg?

(64) Coordinates

Learning objective
Read and record the vocabulary of position, direction and movement, using the four compass directions to describe movement about a grid.

Type of starter
Refresh

Resources
A grid on the whiteboard marked from 0 to 5 along the x axis and A to E along the y axis; five different shapes made from coloured paper, which can be fitted onto the grid to cover multiple squares; Blue-Tack®

No set answers

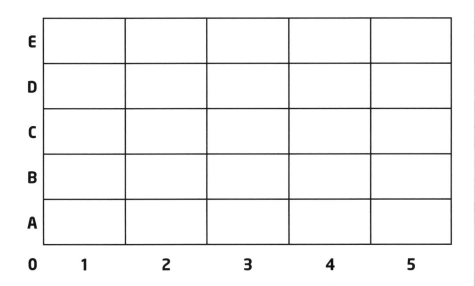

Point to the grid and remind the children of how to read it. Point to a square and ask the children to say its coordinates.

Fix one of the shapes onto the grid and ask:

1. Tell me a square which is covered by this shape.

2. Now tell me some more.

3. Which squares are not covered by this shape?

Repeat for the other shapes.

BLOCK D

(65) Drawing and measuring lines

Resources
A ruler for each child marked in centimetres and half centimetres; sheets of A4 paper

Learning objective
Read, to the nearest division and half-division, scales that are numbered or partially numbered; use the information to measure and draw to a suitable degree of accuracy.

Type of starter
Refine

Mental strategy
Make sure that the children understand that, when drawing a line, they begin at the zero point on the ruler.

No set answers

Provide each child with a sheet of paper and a ruler. Ask them to draw a line with the measurement that you say and write the measurement by the line. Then ask the children to swap papers with a partner to measure the lines and check that they are accurate. Say:

1. Draw a line that is 5cm long.

2. Draw a line that is 9cm long.

3. Draw a line that is 2cm long.

4. Draw a line that is 6cm long.

5. Draw a line that is 11cm long.

6. Draw a line that is $3\frac{1}{2}$ cm long.

7. Draw a line that is $8\frac{1}{2}$ cm long.

8. Draw a line that is $1\frac{1}{2}$ cm long.

9. Draw a line that is $10\frac{1}{2}$ cm long.

10. Draw a line that is $4\frac{1}{2}$ cm long.

BLOCK D

 Cake making

Learning objective	**Resources**
Know the relationships between kilometres and metres, metres and centimetres, kilograms and grams, litres and millilitres; choose and use appropriate units to estimate, measure and record measurements.	A simple cake recipe written on the board (see below); individual whiteboards and pens
Type of starter	
Rehearse	
Mental strategy	
Children will need to use their knowledge of multiplication tables and their understanding of converting metric units. Check that they understand, for example, that 100g can also be written as 0.1kg.	

Write and display a simple recipe on the whiteboard. For example:

100g flour

100g sugar

100g butter

2 eggs

Ask the children to write out the recipe to make the following number of cakes. When you say 'show me', they should hold up their boards for you to check. Say:

1. Write the recipe for making 2 cakes.

2. Write the recipe for making 4 cakes.

3. Write the recipe for making 3 cakes.

For the following cakes ask them to convert the units into kilograms:

4. Write the recipe for making 10 cakes.

5. Write the recipe for making 5 cakes.

6. Write the recipe for making 6 cakes.

Answers

1. 200g flour; 200g sugar; 200g butter; 4 eggs.

2. 400g flour; 400g sugar; 400g butter; 8 eggs.

3. 300g flour; 300g sugar; 300g butter; 6 eggs.

4. 1kg flour; 1kg sugar; 1kg butter; 20 eggs.

5. 0.5kg flour; 0.5kg sugar; 0.5kg butter; 10 eggs.

6. 0.6kg flour; 0.6kg sugar; 0.6kg butter; 6 eggs.

(67) Target totals

Resources	Learning objective
A board or flipchart; pencils and paper	Add or subtract mentally combinations of one-digit and two-digit numbers.
	Type of starter Rehearse
	Mental strategy Use the first example as a reminder of addition skills previously taught (eg putting the larger number first, making multiples of 10, partitioning and recombining).

Answers

1. 9 + 7 + 4
2. 9 + 7 + 3
3. 9 + 7 or 9 + 3 + 4
4. 9 + 7 + 3 + 4
5. 11 + 6 or
    11 + 4 + 2
6. 6 + 4 + 2
7. 11 + 6 + 4
8. 11 + 6 + 4 + 2

Divide the class into mixed-ability pairs.

Write the numbers 3, 4, 7 and 9. Ask the children to make 14 by adding two or more numbers. Set more target totals:

1. 20
2. 19
3. 16
4. 23

Now write the numbers 2, 4, 6 and 11. Ask the children to make:

5. 17
6. 12
7. 21
8. 23

(68) # Shoe shop add and subtract

Learning objective
Develop and use written methods to record, support or explain addition and subtraction of two-digit and three-digit numbers.

Type of starter
Refine

Mental strategy
Encourage the children to use mental strategies for addition and subtraction where possible. They may wish to use empty number lines to mark out the additions and subtractions.

Resources
Individual whiteboards and pens

Explain to the children that they will be solving some word problems that involve the addition or subtraction of two-digit numbers. For each problem, ask the children to write their method and show the answer on their whiteboards. When you say 'show me', they should hold up their boards for you to check.

Invite individuals to write their method on the class whiteboard. Discuss the different methods and point out where these can be simplified.

1. The shoe shop has 67 new boxes of slippers to put on the shelf. There are already 54 boxes of slippers. How many slippers are there in total?

2. There are 92 pairs of trainers on the shelf. On Saturday the shop assistants sell 48 pairs of trainers. How many pairs of trainers are there now?

3. The manager of the shop counts 45 pairs of shoe laces on the stand. Then a delivery of 86 pairs of shoe laces is received. How many pairs of shoe laces does the shop have now?

4. There are 23 pairs of Wellington boots. The manager made a mistake and ordered another 68 pairs of Wellington boots. How many pairs of Wellington boots are there now?

5. Altogether there are 92 pairs of sandals. On Saturday the shop sells 25 boxes of sandals. On Monday the shop sells 31 pairs of sandals. How many pairs of sandals are there left in the shop?

Answers
1. 121
2. 44
3. 131
4. 91
5. 36

⟨69⟩ **Multiplication and division**

Resources
A board or flipchart; paper for writing informal methods

Learning objective
Use practical and informal written methods to multiply and divide two-digit numbers (eg 13 × 3, 50 ÷ 4); round remainders up or down, depending on the context.

Type of starter
Reason

Mental strategy
Encourage the children to use their multiplication table facts to find answers. If children need further help, suggest that they use an empty number line to count up or back in equal jumps.

Answers

1. 36

2. 3 remainder 1

3. 9 trays
   (33 ÷ 4 = 8 remainder 1)

4. 4 (44 ÷ 10 = 4 remainder 4)

5. 80

Explain to the children that they will be solving some word problems that need multiplication or division to find the answers. The children can write informal methods where they cannot carry out the calculation mentally.

Ask the children to explain how they carried out each calculation and write the responses on the board so that other children can compare these with how they worked. Say:

1. There are 12 tangerines in a packet. How many tangerines are there in 3 packets?

2. Bob has 16 marbles. He shares these between himself and four friends. How many marbles do they have each? Are there any left over?

3. The baker makes 33 loaves. The loaves are packed in trays of 4. How many trays does the baker need to pack the loaves?

4. Mr Smith has 44 exercise books to give out to the 10 new children in his class. If he gives each child the same number of books, how many are left over?

5. There are 16 pencils in each jar. How many pencils are there in 5 jars?

(70) Pieces of 8

Learning objective
Find unit fractions of numbers and quantities (eg $^1/_2$, $^1/_3$, $^1/_4$ and $^1/_6$ of 12 litres).

Type of starter
Refresh

Mental strategy
Draw a rectangle divided into eighths.

Resources
A board or flipchart

Emphasise that each section of the rectangle is 'one of the eight equal parts'.

Ask individuals to:

1.   Fill 2 eighths with 'spots'.

2.   Fill 4 eighths with 'stripes'.

3.   Fill 1 eighth with 'curls'.

Then ask:

4.   How many eighths are there?

5.   What fraction of the shape has 'spots'? (Encourage equivalents.)

6.   What fraction has 'stripes'? (Encourage equivalents.)

7.   How many eighths are blank?

8.   If I took away the 'curly' eighth, what fraction of the rectangle would be left?

9.   If I took away the blank eighth, what fraction of the rectangle would be left?

10.   If I put spots into the blank eighth, what fraction would then be 'spotty'?

11.   What fraction would be left if I took away the 'striped' part?

Answers

1-3. N/A

4.   8

5. $^2/_8$ or $^1/_4$

6. $^4/_8$ or $^2/_4$ or $^1/_2$

7.   1

8. $^7/_8$

9. $^7/_8$

10. $^3/_8$

11. $^4/_8$ or $^2/_4$ or $^1/_2$

BLOCK D

(71) **Reflections**

Resources
A 6x6 grid drawn on the board, with a mirror line from top to bottom in the centre of it; squared paper

Learning objective
Draw and complete shapes with reflective symmetry; draw the reflection of a shape in a mirror line along one side.

Type of starter
Read

Mental strategy
Ask the children to explain how they worked out the reflection each time.

Answers

1.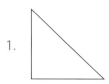

2.

3.

4.

5.

Provide each child with some squared paper. Ask them to draw a letter d on the left-hand side of the mirror with the down stroke of the letter against the mirror line.

Ask them to reflect the letter in the mirror. Then ask: *What letter have you drawn?* (The letter b.) Invite a child to draw what they have done on the class grid. Repeat this for other reflections, each time with the shape lying against the left-hand side of the mirror line:

1.

2.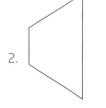

3.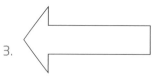

4.

5.

(72) Choose the numbers calculations

Learning objective
Represent the information in a puzzle or problem using numbers, images or diagrams; use these to find a solution and present it in context, where appropriate using £.p notation or units of measure.

Type of starter
Reason

Mental strategy
Encourage the children to write their number sentence then work mentally, recalling number facts that they know.

Resources
A board or flipchart

Ask the children to use three of the numbers each time to write three different addition and subtraction sentences:

1. 3, 6, 8, 13.

2. 4, 7, 9, 15.

Answers
These may include:

1. 13 – 8 + 6 = 11 and so on.

2. 9 + 15 – 4 = 20 and so on.

(73) Addition and subtraction facts Unit 3

Learning objective
Use knowledge of number operations and corresponding inverses, including doubling and halving, to estimate and check calculations.

Type of starter
Refine

Mental strategy
Stress the usefulness of 'counting up' when subtracting numbers that are close together.

Resources
A board or flipchart

Write 19 + 7 = and 32 – 28 =. Ask for volunteers to write an addition fact and a subtraction fact from each of the two examples on the board.

Ask the children to make an addition fact from:

1. 24 – 19 = 5   3. 85 – 78 = 7

2. 69 – 65 = 4   4. 102 – 97 = 5

Ask the children to make a subtraction fact from:

5. 15 + 8 = 23   7. 36 + 24 = 60

6. 22 + 14 = 36   8. 23 + 49 = 72

Answers
1. 19 + 5 = 24 **or** 5 + 19 = 24
2. 65 + 4 = 69 **or** 4 + 65 = 69
3. 78 + 7 = 85 **or** 7 + 78 = 85
4. 97 + 5 = 102 **or** 5 + 97 = 102
5. 23 – 15 = 8 **or** 23 – 8 = 15
6. 36 – 22 = 14 **or** 36 – 14 = 22
7. 60 – 36 = 24 **or** 60 – 24 = 36
8. 72 – 49 = 23 **or** 72 – 23 = 49

BLOCK D

(74) Number sentences

Resources	Learning objective
A board or flipchart; paper and pencils for each pair	Develop and use written methods to record, support or explain addition and subtraction of two-digit and three-digit numbers.

Type of starter
Reason

Answers

Possible answers might include:

1.   12 + 14 = 26
2.   28 + 12 = 40
3.   28 + 12 = 26 + 14
4.   40 – 14 = 26
5.   40 = 28 + 12
6.   26 – 14 = 12

Write the following numbers:

12, 14, 26, 28 and 40.

Ask the children to work in pairs to make number sentences using these numbers. For example, 40 – 28 = 12.

(75) Tens

Resources
None

Learning objective
Use practical and informal written methods to multiply and divide two-digit numbers (eg 13 × 3, 50 ÷ 4); round remainders up or down, depending on the context.

Type of starter
Refine

Mental strategy
Stress that when we make the number bigger by multiplying, the digits move to the left. When we make a number smaller by dividing, the digits move to the right.

Answers

1.   50
2.   80
3.   200
4.   600
5.   7
6.   200
7.   350
8.   300
9.   10
10. 100

1.   5 × 10
2.   8 × 10
3.   20 × 10
4.   60 × 10
5.   70 ÷ 10

6.   40 × 5
7.   70 × 5
8.   60 × 5
9.   80 ÷ ? = 8
10. 900 ÷ ? = 9

BLOCK D

(76) **Right shift**

Learning objective Understand that division is the inverse of multiplication and vice versa; use this to derive and record related multiplication and division number sentences. **Type of starter** Refresh	**Resources** A board or flipchart with prepared HTU columns

Write 50. Ask a child to make it 10 times smaller, writing the answer in the correct columns.

Write 300 and ask for it to be made a hundred times smaller.

Repeat for the following, asking a child to write each answer in the correct columns:

1. 70, make 10 times smaller
2. 200, make 100 times smaller
3. 40, make 10 times smaller
4. 60, make 10 times smaller
5. 900, make 10 times smaller
6. 500, make 100 times smaller

Answers

1. 7
2. 2
3. 4
4. 6
5. 90
6. 5

(77) **Reading grams**

Learning objective Read, to the nearest division and half-division, scales that are numbered or partially numbered; use the information to measure and draw to a suitable degree of accuracy. **Type of starter** Read **Mental strategy** Children will need to understand that mid-way between two marks gives a reading that includes 5g.	**Resources** A dial scale drawn on the board, with divisions in 10g increments from 0 to 100g

Look together at the weighing scale diagram. Ask: *What is the scale?* Agree that it increases by 10g each time. Explain that you will point to a position on the weighing scale diagram and will ask the children to say what the reading is. Point to:

1. 10g
2. 50g
3. 100g
4. 40g
5. 45g
6. 35g
7. 95g
8. 35g
9. 15g
10. 75g

No set answers

(78) **Take five**

Resources A teaching clock	**Learning objective** Read the time on a 12-hour digital clock and to the nearest 5 minutes on an analogue clock; calculate time intervals and find start or end times for a given time interval. **Type of starter** Rehearse

No set answers

Count in 5s to 60 and back again.

Move the minute hand round the clock face as the children say together '5 minutes past', '10 minutes past' up to '30 minutes past' (or 'half past').

Move the minute hand to specific times and invite the children say together:

1.   10 minutes past.

2.   20 minutes past.

3.   5 minutes past.

4.   15 minutes past (or quarter past).

5.   30 minutes past (or half past).

Move the minute hand from half past onwards as the children say together '25 minutes to', '20 minutes to' up to the hour.

Move the minute hand to specific times and invite the children say together:

6.   20 minutes to.

7.   5 minutes to.

8.   25 minutes to.

9.   15 minutes to (or quarter to).

10.   10 minutes to.

Select times at random around the clock to test the children.

BLOCK E

Unit 1

100 Mental Maths Starters				100 Maths Lessons		
Page	Objective	Activity title	Starter type	Unit	Lesson	Page
73	Derive and recall all addition and subtraction facts for each number to 20, sums and differences of multiples of 10 and number pairs that total 100.	(79) Addition bonds	Rehearse	1	1	171
73	Derive and recall all addition and subtraction facts for each number to 20, sums and differences of multiples of 10 and number pairs that total 100.	(80) Quick subtraction	Recall	1	2	172
74	Derive and recall multiplication facts for the two-, three-, four-, five-, six- and ten-times tables and the corresponding division facts; recognise multiples of 2, 5 or 10 up to 1000.	(81) Multiples of 2	Rehearse	1	4	173
74	Use practical and informal written methods to multiply and divide two-digit numbers (eg 13 × 3, 50 ÷ 4); round remainders up or down, depending on the context.	(82) Count in fours	Rehearse	1	5	174
75	Use practical and informal written methods to multiply and divide two-digit numbers (eg 13 × 3, 50 ÷ 4); round remainders up or down, depending on the context.	(83) Money problems	Rehearse	1	9	177
76	Identify patterns and relationships involving numbers or shapes, and use these to solve problems.	(84) Addition grid	Reason	1	10	177
77	Find unit fractions of numbers and quantities (eg $1/2$, $1/3$, $1/4$ and $1/6$ of 12 litres).	(85) Fractions	Read	1	12	179
77	Find unit fractions of numbers and quantities (eg $1/2$, $1/3$, $1/4$ and $1/6$ of 12 litres).	(86) Fractions of shapes	Rehearse	1	13	179

Unit 2

100 Mental Maths Starters				100 Maths Lessons		
Page	Objective	Activity title	Starter type	Unit	Lesson	Page
78	Read and write proper fractions (eg $3/7$, $9/10$), interpreting the denominator as the parts of a whole and the numerator as the number of parts; identify and estimate fractions of shapes; use diagrams to compare fractions and establish equivalents.	(87) Half and half again	Rehearse	2	1 or 2	190
78	Derive and recall multiplication facts for the two-, three-, four-, five-, six- and ten-times tables and the corresponding division facts; recognise multiples of 2, 5 or 10 up to 1000.	(88) Multiples of 4	Rehearse	2	3	191
79	Multiply one-digit and two-digit numbers by 10 or 100, and describe the effect.	(89) ÷ 10	Recall	2	6	193

Unit 2 ...continued

	100 Mental Maths Starters				100 Maths Lessons		
Page	Objective	Activity title	Starter type	Unit	Lesson	Page
79	Use practical and informal written methods to multiply and divide two-digit numbers (eg 13 × 3, 50 ÷ 4); round remainders up or down, depending on the context.	90 Rounding up or down	Reason	2	8	194
80	Understand that division is the inverse of multiplication and vice versa; use this to derive and record related multiplication and division number sentences.	91 ×4 and ÷4	Reason	2	10	195
80	Find unit fractions of numbers and quantities (eg $1/2$, $1/3$, $1/4$ and $1/6$ of 12 litres).	92 Fraction money word problems	Rehearse	2	12	196
81	Solve one-step and two-step problems involving numbers, money or measures, including time, choosing and carrying out appropriate calculations.	93 What coins do I have?	Rehearse	2	13	197
82	Solve one-step and two-step problems involving numbers, money or measures, including time, choosing and carrying out appropriate calculations.	94 Pocket money	Rehearse	2	15	199

Unit 3

	100 Mental Maths Starters				100 Maths Lessons		
Page	Objective	Activity title	Starter type	Unit	Lesson	Page
83	Partition three-digit numbers into multiples of 100, 10 and 1 in different ways.	95 Left shift	Refresh	3	1	207
83	Identify patterns and relationships involving numbers or shapes, and use these to solve problems.	96 Magic square	Reason	3	3	209
84	Read and write proper fractions (eg $3/7$, $9/10$), interpreting the denominator as the parts of a whole and the numerator as the number of parts; identify and estimate fractions of shapes; use diagrams to compare fractions and establish equivalents.	97 Shape fractions	Rehearse	3	7	212
84	Derive and recall multiplication facts for the two-, three-, four-, five-, six- and ten-times tables and the corresponding division facts; recognise multiples of 2, 5 or 10 up to 1000.	98 Steps of 5	Rehearse	3	9	213
85	Find unit fractions of numbers and quantities (eg $1/2$, $1/3$, $1/4$ and $1/6$ of 12 litres).	99 Units fractions of quantities	Refresh	3	10	213
86	Develop and use written methods to record, support or explain addition and subtraction of two-digit and three-digit numbers.	100 Addition and subtraction word problems	Rehearse	3	12	215
87	Use practical and informal written methods to multiply and divide two-digit numbers (eg 13 × 3, 50 ÷ 4).	101 Remainders	Read	3	13	216
87	Solve one-step and two-step problems involving numbers, money or measures, including time, choosing and carrying out appropriate calculations.	102 Two-step problems	Rehearse	3	15	217

BLOCK E

79 Addition bonds

Learning objective Derive and recall all addition and subtraction facts for each number to 20, sums and differences of multiples of 10 and number pairs that total 100.	**Resources** None

Type of starter
Rehearse

Mental strategy
Emphasise counting on from the larger number (eg 5 + 13 = 13 + 5 = 18) and using near doubles (eg 7 + 6 = 12 + 1 = 13).

This is a rapid recall session for addition facts with numbers up to 20:

					Answers			
1.	3 + 3	9.	1 + 15		1.	6	9.	16
2.	10 + 4	10.	6 + 3		2.	14	10.	9
3.	8 + 12	11.	4 + 12		3.	20	11.	16
4.	6 + 0	12.	17 + 2		4.	6	12.	19
5.	5 + 4	13.	9 + 9		5.	9	13.	18
6.	7 + 8	14.	6 + 6		6.	15	14.	12
7.	9 + 3	15.	7 + 7		7.	12	15.	14
8.	3 + 11				8.	14		

80 Quick subtraction

Learning objective Derive and recall all addition and subtraction facts for each number to 20, sums and differences of multiples of 10 and number pairs that total 100.	**Resources** None

Type of starter
Recall

This is a rapid recall session for subtraction facts with numbers up to 20:

					Answers			
1.	4 - 2	9.	8 - 4		1.	2	9.	4
2.	8 - 1	10.	5 - 3		2.	7	10.	2
3.	19 - 1	11.	12 - 8		3.	18	11.	4
4.	19 - 2	12.	11 - 6		4.	17	12.	5
5.	6 - 5	13.	18 - 6		5.	1	13.	12
6.	6 - 6	14.	12 - 5		6.	0	14.	7
7.	10 - 5	15.	9 - 3		7.	5	15.	6
8.	10 - 9				8.	1		

BLOCK E

(81) Multiples of 2

Resources A board or flipchart	**Learning objective** Derive and recall multiplication facts for the two-, three-, four-, five-, six- and 10-times tables and the corresponding division facts; recognise multiples of 2, 5 or 10 up to 1000. **Type of starter** Rehearse
No set answers	Draw a 'clock face' on the board with the numbers 1–10 arranged randomly in a circle. Write '×2' in the centre. The children face the board and, in unison, say each multiplication fact three times in succession. This will encourage children who are unsure the first time to join in the repetitions.

(82) Count in fours

Resources A number line drawn on the board; a pointer	**Learning objective** Use practical and informal written methods to multiply and divide two-digit numbers (eg 13 × 3, 50 ÷ 4); round remainders up or down, depending on the context. **Type of starter** Rehearse

Answers

1. 12
2. 20
3. 28
4. 8
5. 4
6. 36
7. 16
8. 24
9. 40
10. 32

Write a 1–9 number line on the board.

Ask individual children to write the multiples of 4 under the line.

Practise counting in fours. Say the four-times table in order. Point to numbers out of sequence.

Ask the whole class questions. For example:

1. 3 times 4.

2. 5 multiplied by 4.

3. 7 times 4.

4. Twice 4 is.

5. 1 group of 4.

6. 9 multiplied by 4.

7. 4 times 4.

8. The product of 6 and 4 is?

9. 10 times 4.

10. 8 multiplied by 4.

(83) Money problems

Learning objective
Use practical and informal written methods to multiply and divide two-digit numbers (eg 13 × 3, 50 ÷ 4); round remainders up or down, depending on the context.

Type of starter
Rehearse

Mental strategy
Remind the children that to find the cost of two items, we double (×2) the cost of one item.

Ask the children how they would find the cost of five items. Establish that they should multiply by 5.

Ask the children to find the cost of three items. Explain that this could be done by adding or by multiplying.

Resources
Large pictures of coins to 50p, displayed for the whole class to see

1. 1 costs 10p. 2 will cost?

2. 1 costs 3p. 2 will cost?

3. 1 costs 5p. 2 will cost?

4. 1 costs 12p. 2 will cost?

5. 1 costs 8p. 2 will cost?

6. 1 costs 11p. 2 will cost?

7. 1 costs 2p. 3 will cost?

8. 1 costs 5p. 3 will cost?

9. 1 costs 10p. 3 will cost?

10. 1 costs 4p. 3 will cost?

11. 1 costs 13p. 3 will cost?

12. 1 costs 7p. 3 will cost?

13. 1 costs 14p. 3 will cost?

14. 1 costs 2p. 5 will cost?

15. 1 costs 10p. 5 will cost?

Answers
1. 20p
2. 6p
3. 10p
4. 24p
5. 16p
6. 22p
7. 6p
8. 15p
9. 30p
10. 12p
11. 39p
12. 21p
13. 42p
14. 10p
15. 50p

(84) Addition grid

Resources
One large addition grid (see below)

Learning objective
Identify patterns and relationships involving numbers or shapes, and use these to solve problems.

Type of starter
Reason

Answers

1. even
2. odd
3. even
4. odd
5. odd
6. odd
7. even
8. even
9. odd
10. even
11. odd
12. even

Write the following addition grid on the board:

+	1	3	5	7	9
2					
4					
6					
8					
10					

Ask targeted individuals to fill in the cells.

Make sure the children understand that all the answers in this grid are odd numbers.

Encourage general statements about adding odd and even numbers. For example,

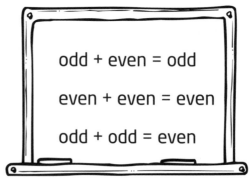

odd + even = odd

even + even = even

odd + odd = even

Ask children to say whether the answers to these addition questions are odd or even:

1. 3 + 5
2. 14 + 15
3. 10 + 12
4. 16 + 19
5. 18 + 11
6. 17 + 12
7. 9 + 11
8. 6 + 12
9. 13 + 14
10. 15 + 13
11. 10 + 11
12. 19 + 13

(85) Fractions

	Resources
Learning objective Find unit fractions of numbers and quantities (eg $\frac{1}{2}$, $\frac{1}{3}$, $\frac{1}{4}$ and $\frac{1}{6}$ of 12 litres). **Type of starter** Read **Mental strategy** Children may use facts they already know, such as doubles and halves of numbers. Encourage them to use table facts to find division facts.	None

Ask the children to tell you how they would find a quantity using division. Now say:

1. What is half of 30? How did you work that out?

2. There are 26 grapes. Paul eats half of them. How many are left?

3. Sara makes 30 badges. She gives $\frac{1}{3}$ of them to May. How many badges does May have?

4. How would you work out $\frac{1}{8}$ of 48?

5. Which is more: $\frac{1}{8}$ of 36kg or $\frac{1}{6}$ of 22kg?

Answers
1. 15
2. 13
3. 10
4. $48 \div 4 = 12$ and $12 \div 2 = 6$
5. $\frac{1}{2}$ of 22kg

(86) Fractions of shapes

	Resources
Learning objective Find unit fractions of numbers and quantities (eg $\frac{1}{2}$, $\frac{1}{3}$, $\frac{1}{4}$ and $\frac{1}{6}$ of 12 litres). **Type of starter** Rehearse **Mental strategy** Remind the children to use doubles and halves that they know, and table facts, to find the solutions.	Squared paper

Ask the children to draw rectangles with the number of squares that you say and shade in the given fractions:

1. Draw a rectangle with 8 squares. Shade $\frac{1}{2}$.

2. Draw a rectangle with 12 squares. Shade $\frac{1}{3}$.

3. Draw a rectangle with 12 squares. Shade $\frac{1}{6}$.

4. Draw a rectangle with 20 squares. Shade $\frac{1}{5}$.

5. Draw a rectangle with 20 squares. Shade $\frac{1}{10}$.

6. Draw a rectangle with 20 squares. Shade $\frac{1}{4}$.

7. Draw a rectangle with 24 squares. Shade $\frac{1}{3}$.

8. Draw a rectangle with 24 squares. Shade $\frac{1}{4}$.

Answers
1. 4 squares
2. 4 squares
3. 2 squares
4. 4 squares
5. 2 squares
6. 5 squares
7. 8 squares
8. 6 squares

BLOCK E

(87) Half and half again

Resources	**Learning objective**
Individual whiteboards and pens	Read and write proper fractions (eg $^3/_7$, $^9/_{10}$), interpreting the denominator as the parts of a whole and the numerator as the number of parts; identify and estimate fractions of shapes; use diagrams to compare fractions and establish equivalents.

Type of starter
Rehearse

Mental strategy
Encourage the children to use what they already know. For example, if they know that half of 8 is 4, then they can work out that half of 80 is 40.

Answers

1.	5	5.	16
2.	10	6.	20
3.	12	7.	24
4.	15	8.	25

Explain that you will say a number. Ask the children to find a quarter of it by halving the number, then halving it again. When you say 'show me', the children hold up their boards for you to see. Say:

1.	20	5.	64
2.	40	6.	80
3.	48	7.	96
4.	60	8.	100

(88) Multiples of 4

Resources	**Learning objective**
A board or flipchart	Derive and recall multiplication facts for the two-, three-, four-, five-, six- and 10-times tables and the corresponding division facts; recognise multiples of 2, 5 or 10 up to 1000.

Type of starter
Rehearse

Answers

1.	8	6.	36
2.	24	7.	16
3.	4	8.	40
4.	32	9.	28
5.	12	10.	20

Build up the four-times table on the board. Look at the units pattern. Notice that all answers are even numbers.

Say the table together several times. Count in fours forwards and backwards.

Ask individuals to answer questions while the table can be seen. For example:

1.	2 × 4	6.	9 × 4
2.	6 × 4	7.	4 × 4
3.	1 × 4	8.	10 × 4
4.	8 × 4	9.	7 × 4
5.	3 × 4	10.	5 × 4

Erase the better-known answers, then repeat.

(89) ÷10

Learning objective	**Resources**
Multiply one-digit and two-digit numbers by 10 or 100, and describe the effect.	A board or flipchart
Type of starter	
Recall	

Recite the ten-times table together, saying each complete fact (eg '1 times 10 is 10').

Emphasise that division is the inverse of multiplication.

Recall the division facts for the ten-times table. Ask:

1. How many 10s make 50?
2. How many 10s make 70?
3. 20 divided by 10 equals?
4. 100 divided by 10 equals?
5. Divide 40 by 10.
6. Divide 60 by 10.
7. How many 10s make 90?
8. 10 divided by 10 equals?

Answers

1.	5	5.	4
2.	7	6.	6
3.	2	7.	9
4.	10	8.	1

(90) Rounding up or down

Learning objective	**Resources**
Use practical and informal written methods to multiply and divide two-digit numbers (eg 13 × 3, 50 ÷ 4); round remainders up or down, depending on the context.	Paper for jottings
Type of starter	
Reason	
Mental strategy	
Encourage the children to use table facts to help them to find the answers. If children struggle, provide number lines so that they can count back or forwards in groups.	

Explain that these word problems may have remainders. The children must decide whether to round the answer up or down and explain why they made that decision. Say:

1. There are 50 cakes to be put into boxes. Each box holds 4 cakes. How many boxes are needed so that all the cakes are packed?
2. 32 children are going to the cinema. They are going in cars. Each car will hold 3 children. How many cars are needed?
3. Pencils come in boxes of 10. The factory has made 155 pencils. Each box must be filled. How many boxes can the factory fill? How many more pencils does the factory need to make to fill another box?
4. Sally has 45 cards. She puts these into bundles of 4. How many bundles does she have?
5. 4 friends decide to share out 30 grapes. How many do they have each?

Answers

1. 13
2. 11
3. 15; 5 more.
4. 11
5. 7

BLOCK E

(91) ×4 and ÷4

Resources	Learning objective
None	Understand that division is the inverse of multiplication and vice versa; use this to derive and record related multiplication and division number sentences.
	Type of starter Reason

Answers

1.	12	9.	10
2.	3	10.	1
3.	28	11.	20
4.	7	12.	32
5.	36	13.	6
6.	4	14.	2
7.	8	15.	9
8.	24	16.	16

Ask the children for a division fact from 5 × 4 = 20. Use this to remind them of the connection between multiplication and division.

1. 3 × 4
2. How many 4s in 12?
3. 7 × 4
4. Divide 28 by 4.
5. 9 × 4
6. How many 4s make 16?
7. How many 4s make 32?
8. Multiply 6 by 4.
9. Divide 40 by 4.
10. How many 4s make 4?
11. 5 × 4
12. 8 multiplied by 4.
13. Share 24 between 4.
14. Divide 8 by 4.
15. How many 4s make 36?
16. 4 × 4

(92) Fraction money word problems

Resources	Learning objective
Paper for jottings	Find unit fractions of numbers and quantities (eg $\frac{1}{2}$, $\frac{1}{3}$, $\frac{1}{4}$ and $\frac{1}{6}$ of 12 litres).
	Type of starter Rehearse
	Mental strategy Encourage the children to use table facts to find the answers. For example, if they know that $\frac{1}{3}$ of 6 is 2, then they can work out that $\frac{1}{3}$ of 60 is 20.

Answers

1. £1.50
2. £4.50
3. £5.25
4. 80p
5. 40p

Ask the children to calculate these fractions mentally. Explain that they can use paper for jottings if needed. Say:

1. I have £3. I give my sister half of the money. How much do we each have?
2. The sports shop has a sale. Everything is half price. How much does a football that was £9 cost now?
3. The sports t-shirt was £10.50. How much is it now?
4. At the toy shop some items are a quarter of their original price. A jigsaw was £3.20. How much is it now?
5. The supermarket has a special offer on juice. There is a third off its original price. The price was 60p. How much is the juice now?

BLOCK E

(93) What coins do I have?

Learning objective
Solve one-step and two-step problems involving numbers, money or measures, including time, choosing and carrying out appropriate calculations.

Type of starter
Rehearse

Mental strategy
Encourage the children to work out the highest value coin first.

Resources
Large pictures of coins to 50p displayed for the whole class to see (or one of each coin between two, with children working in pairs)

What coins do I have if:

1. I have 3 coins with a total value of 17p?

2. I have 3 coins with a total value of 23p?

3. I have 3 coins with a total value of 31p?

4. I have 3 coins with a total value of 53p?

5. I have 4 coins with a total value of 18p?

6. I have 4 coins with a total value of 85p?

7. I have 4 coins with a total value of 66p?

8. I have 5 coins with a total value of 37p?

Answers
1. 10p, 5p, 2p

2. 20p, 2p, 1p

3. 20p, 10p, 1p

4. 50p, 2p, 1p

5. 10p, 5p, 2p, 1p

6. 50p, 20p, 10p, 5p

7. 50p, 10p, 5p, 1p

8. 10p, 10p, 10p, 5p, 2p **or** 20p, 10p, 5p, 1p, 1p

(94) **Pocket money**

Resources	**Learning objective**
None	Solve one-step and two-step problems involving numbers, money or measures, including time, choosing and carrying out appropriate calculations.
	Type of starter
	Rehearse

Answers

1. 24p
2. 15p
3. 3p
4. 7p
5. 2p coins
6. 30p
7. 45p
8. 50p
9. 5 weeks
10. 88p
11. 27p
12. 7p
13. 8p
14. 22p
15. 75p

Repeating the question, using different wording, may be helpful.

Allow time for less able children to work out the answer.

1. How much do two pencils cost if each pencil costs 12p?

2. I have 7p and you have 8p. How much do we have altogether?

3. I had 20p, then spent 17p. How much do I have left?

4. Two lollies cost 14p altogether. How much was each lolly?

5. I have six identical coins. I have 12p. What coins do I have?

6. I had 40p, but then lost 10p. How much do I have left?

7. Matthew had two 20p coins and one 5p coin. How much did he have?

8. Michael had three 10p coins and one 20p coin. How much did he have?

9. If I saved 10p each week, how long would it take me to save 50p?

10. If I had one of every coin from 1p to 50p, how much would I have?

11. I have 12p and you have 15p. How much do we have altogether?

12. I had 25p, then spent 18p. How much do I have left?

13. Pencils cost 14p each. I wanted two, but only had 20p. How much more did I need?

14. My friend and I had 50p between us. I had 28p. How much did he have?

15. I saved 25p each week for 3 weeks. How much had I saved?

BLOCK E

(95) Left shift

Learning objective
Partition three-digit numbers into multiples of 100, 10 and 1 in different ways.

Type of starter
Refresh

Mental strategy
Remind the children that zeros are needed to hold the digits in place.

Resources
A board or flipchart with prepared HTU columns

Write each number in turn on the HTU chart and then ask individual children to write the answers in the correct columns underneath:

1. 5, make 10 times larger.
2. 40, make 10 times larger.
3. 9, make 100 times larger.
4. 7, make 100 times larger.
5. 2, make 10 times larger.
6. 30, make 10 times larger.
7. 80, make 10 times larger.
8. 3, make 100 times larger.
9. 8, make 10 times larger.
10. 60, make 10 times larger.

Answers
1. 50
2. 400
3. 900
4. 700
5. 20
6. 300
7. 800
8. 300
9. 80
10. 600

(96) Magic square

Learning objective
Identify patterns and relationships involving numbers or shapes, and use these to solve problems.

Type of starter
Reason

Mental strategy
Suggest children place a number in the centre square first and then work around it.

Resources
A board or flipchart; paper and pencils for each pair

Divide the class into mixed-ability pairs.

Draw a 3x3 grid on the board.

Ask the children to copy it and then to create a 'magic' square in which each row, column and diagonal gives a total of 15. They can only use the numbers 1–9 once to complete the square.

Answers
One solution is shown below. Many others are possible.

6	7	2
1	5	9
8	3	4

BLOCK E

(97) Shape fractions

Resources
A whole-class grid on which shapes can be drawn and then erased; squared paper

Learning objective
Read and write proper fractions (eg $^3/_7$, $^9/_{10}$), interpreting the denominator as the parts of a whole and the numerator as the number of parts; identify and estimate fractions of shapes; use diagrams to compare fractions and establish equivalents.

Type of starter
Rehearse

Mental strategy
Discuss why, usually, there is more than one way to do the shading.

Remind children of what the numerator and denominator mean. Encourage them to work mentally, counting up using the denominator or using table facts.

Answers

1. 6 squares shaded.
2. 9 squares shaded.
3. 6 squares shaded.
4. 20 squares shaded.
5. 9 squares shaded.

Ask the children to draw the rectangle that you say and then shade in the fraction. Once they have completed this ask a child to draw and shade in their rectangle on the whole-class grid so that the children can compare what they did. Say:

1. Draw a rectangle that is 3 by 4. Shade in $^1/_2$.
2. Draw a rectangle that is 6 by 2. Shade in $^3/_4$.
3. Draw a rectangle that is 5 by 2. Shade in $^3/_5$.
4. Draw a rectangle that is 4 by 6. Shade in $^5/_6$.
5. Draw a rectangle that is 8 by 3. Shade in $^3/_8$.

(98) Steps of 5

Resources
A number line drawn on the board or flipchart

Learning objective
Derive and recall multiplication facts for the two-, three-, four-, five-, six- and 10-times tables and the corresponding division facts; recognise multiples of 2, 5 or 10 up to 1000.

Type of starter
Rehearse

Answers

1.	10	6.	50
2.	40	7.	25
3.	15	8.	5
4.	35	9.	30
5.	4	10.	10

Draw a number line. Ask individual children to write multiples of 5 under the line.

When the line is complete, count in fives forwards and backwards. Say the five-times table together. Point to numbers out of sequence.

Remove the number line and ask quick-fire questions:

1. 2 times 5.
2. 8 multiplied by 5.
3. Three 5s are?
4. 7 steps of 5 make?
5. How many 5s make 20?
6. 10 times 5.
7. 5 times itself is?
8. 1 multiplied by 5.
9. The product of 6 and 5 is?
10. Double 5.

■SCHOLASTIC

BLOCK E

 (99) **Unit fractions of quantities**

Learning objective Find unit fractions of numbers and quantities (eg $\frac{1}{2}$, $\frac{1}{3}$, $\frac{1}{4}$ and $\frac{1}{6}$ of 12 litres). **Type of starter** Refresh **Mental strategy** Remind the children that they can use what they know to find a fact that they do not know. For example, $\frac{1}{2}$ of 50 is 25 so $\frac{1}{2}$ of 500 will be 250.	**Resources** Individual whiteboards and pens

Ask the children to find the answer as quickly as they can and write it on their whiteboards.

When you say 'show me', they should hold up their boards for you to see:

1. What is $\frac{1}{2}$ of £30?
2. What is $\frac{1}{4}$ of 100 grams?
3. What is $\frac{1}{3}$ of 12 litres?
4. What is $\frac{1}{6}$ of £48?
5. What is $\frac{1}{10}$ of £20?
6. What is $\frac{1}{4}$ of 32 grams?
7. What is $\frac{1}{5}$ of 35 centimetres?
8. What is $\frac{1}{2}$ of 500 metres?
9. What is $\frac{1}{6}$ of 36 kilometres?
10. What is $\frac{1}{3}$ of 33 kilograms?

Answers
1. £15
2. 25 grams
3. 4 litres
4. £8
5. £2
6. 8 grams
7. 7 centimetres
8. 250 metres
9. 6 kilometres
10. 11 kilograms

BLOCK E

(100) Addition and subtraction word problems

Resources Paper for jottings	**Learning objective** Develop and use written methods to record, support or explain addition and subtraction of two-digit and three-digit numbers. **Type of starter** Rehearse **Mental strategy** Encourage the children to work mentally where they can. They can use column addition or subtraction where the calculation requires it.
Answers 1. £247 2. 394 3. 212 4. 69	Explain that the children will probably need to use paper and pencil methods, and mental calculations to find the answers. For each question, ask some children to write their method on the board for others to see. Remind them that there could be more than one way to solve each problem. Say: 1. Marcus has £372 in his bank account. He decides to buy a new monitor for his computer. This costs him £125. How much money does he have left? 2. There are 238 packets of CD-ROMs in the warehouse. The manager has a delivery of 156 packets of CD-ROMs. How many are there now in total? 3. There are 640 sandwiches in the kitchen. At lunchtime the children eat 428 sandwiches. How many are left? 4. For the school fete the children collect 237 prizes for the lucky dip. At the fete 168 prizes are won. How many prizes are there left over?

(101) Remainders

Resources Paper for jottings	**Learning objective** Use practical and informal written methods to multiply and divide two-digit numbers (eg 13 × 3, 50 ÷ 4). **Type of starter** Read **Mental strategy** Encourage the children to use table facts, where they can, and to record their working carefully.
Answers 1. 11, remainder 2 2. 8 3. 5, remainder 4 4. 12, remainder 2	Write each division on the board. Ask the children to find the answer using practical methods, mental calculations, or written methods. For each question invite children to explain how they found the answer. Say: 1. 35 sheep are put into three pens. How many sheep are there in each pen? How many are left? 2. 46 children decide to go on the visit to the cinema. Each minibus holds 6 children. How many minibuses are needed? 3. 54 pencils are shared between 10 boxes. How many pencils are there in each box? How many are left? 5. 62 sweets are shared between 5 plates. How many sweets are there on each plate? How many are left over?

BLOCK E

 Two-step problems

Learning objective Solve one-step and two-step problems involving numbers, money or measures, including time, choosing and carrying out appropriate calculations. **Type of starter** Rehearse **Mental strategy** Encourage the children to use facts that they know, such as table facts, addition and subtraction facts.	**Resources** Paper for jottings

Explain that the problems all have two steps. Ask the children to make jottings, where necessary, and to be prepared to explain to the other children how they found the answer.

Remind them that there will probably be more than one way to solve each problem. Repeat each problem twice and, if necessary, write the problem on the board. Say:

1. There are 46 books on the bottom shelf and 57 on the top shelf. The librarian removes 27 books. How many are there in total now?

2. The librarian receives 346 new books. She puts these into a box where there are already another 250 books. Another librarian now removes 167 books. How many books are there in the box now?

3. For school lunch the cook makes 234 popadoms. Class 3 eats 36 of the popadoms. Class 4 eats 34 popadoms. How many popadoms are left for the rest of the school to eat?

4. On Mondays to Fridays Charlie eats 4 pieces of fruit. At the weekend he eats 5 pieces on fruit on each day. How many pieces of fruit does Charlie eat in one week?

5. Marisa likes vegetables. At home she eats 3 portions of vegetables each weekday. At the weekend she eats 5 portions of vegetables each day. How many portions of vegetables does Marisa eat in one week?

Answers

1. 76
2. 429
3. 164
4. 30
5. 25

Hundreds, tens and units chart

Hundreds	100	200	300	400	500	600	700	800	900
Tens	10	20	30	40	50	60	70	80	90
Units	1	2	3	4	5	6	7	8	9

Enlarge to at least A3 size for whole-class use.

2D or 3D?

1. triangle

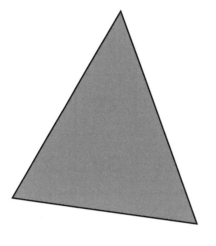

4. hemisphere

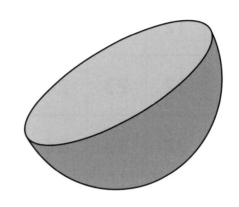

2. cuboid

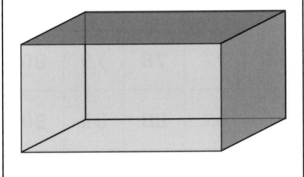

5. hexagon

3. pentagon

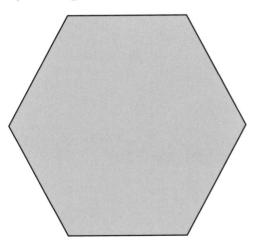

6. prism

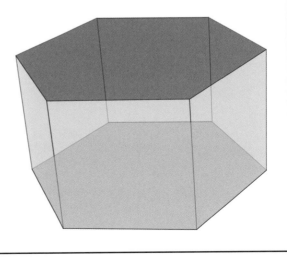

RESOURCE

1–100 square

1	2	3	4	5	6	7	8	9	10
11	12	13	14	15	16	17	18	19	20
21	22	23	24	25	26	27	28	29	30
31	32	33	34	35	36	37	38	39	40
41	42	43	44	45	46	47	48	49	50
51	52	53	54	55	56	57	58	59	60
61	62	63	64	65	66	67	68	69	70
71	72	73	74	75	76	77	78	79	80
81	82	83	84	85	86	87	88	89	90
91	92	93	94	95	96	97	98	99	100

Number fractions

◆ Choose a colour.
◆ Colour two quarters of each shape and write in the spaces.

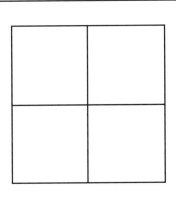

I have coloured two quarters.

I have coloured one half.

$\frac{1}{4} + \frac{1}{4} = \frac{1}{2}$

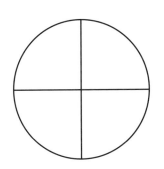

I have coloured two _____.

I have coloured one _____.

$\frac{1}{4} + \frac{1}{4} = $ _____

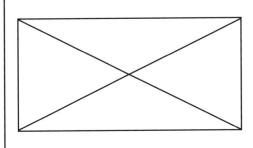

I have coloured two _____.

I have coloured one _____.

$\frac{1}{4} + $ _____ $= $ _____

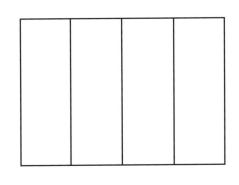

I have coloured _____.

I have coloured _____.

_____ $+$ _____ $=$ _____

Money puzzles

■ Imagine you have three coins. Each coin is worth more than 5p. You can have more than one of the same coin.

■ Write ten different totals that you can make with different combinations of three coins in the space below.

_____ + _____ + _____ = _____

_____ + _____ + _____ = _____

_____ + _____ + _____ = _____

_____ + _____ + _____ = _____

_____ + _____ + _____ = _____

_____ + _____ + _____ = _____

_____ + _____ + _____ = _____

_____ + _____ + _____ = _____

_____ + _____ + _____ = _____

_____ + _____ + _____ = _____

Shape fractions

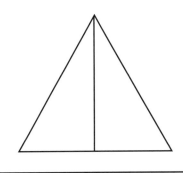	$\frac{1}{2}$ is coloured.
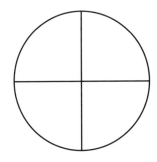	I have coloured $\frac{1}{2}$.
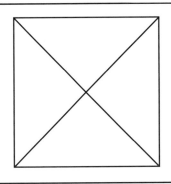	I have coloured $\frac{2}{4} = \frac{1}{2}$.
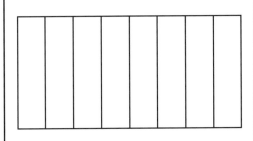	I have coloured $\frac{4}{8} = $ ___ $= \frac{1}{4} + \frac{1}{4}$
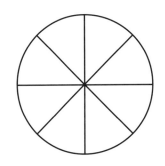	I have coloured $\frac{2}{4} = $ ___

Car colour pictogram

■ The colour of cars that passed by the school on Thursday morning:

blue	●	●	●	●	◗	
red	●	●	●	●	◗	
green	●	●	◜			
silver	●	●	●	●	●	◜
black	●	●	◗			

Key: ● represents 4 cars

Estimate and measure

_____

estimate: ☐   measure: ☐   difference: ☐

_____

estimate: ☐   measure: ☐   difference: ☐

_____

estimate: ☐   measure: ☐   difference: ☐

_____

estimate: ☐   measure: ☐   difference: ☐

_____

estimate: ☐   measure: ☐   difference: ☐

_____

estimate: ☐   measure: ☐   difference: ☐

Score : ☐

Level 2: Oral and mental assessment

Teachers' notes

Time: 20 minutes for each complete paper.

- Children should sit so that they are unable to see each other's work.
- Do not explain questions or read numbers to the children.
- The test may be administered to groups of children or to the whole class.
- There are 20 marks available for each paper.
- The tests consist of 15 oral questions and five practical and oral assessments.
- The oral questions could be administered to a class or to smaller groups, if desired.
- Less confident learners could give their answers orally to a teaching assistant or other adult who could record their answers.
- The oral and practical assessment questions are to be delivered to a maximum of four children. This will enable the adult delivering the assessment to make a more detailed assessment of a child's proficiency and make it possible to identify areas for future development.

Delivering the tests

- Read questions no more than twice to the children.
- Allow five seconds for each answer.
- Answers to be recorded on the answer sheets provided.
- One mark per question: 20 marks total.

Say to the children:

'I am going to read some questions for you to answer. I will read each question twice. You will have five seconds to answer each question.'

'For most of the questions you will write your answer in a box.' [Show example.]

'For some questions you may need to tick the right answer.'

'If you make a mistake, you should cross it out and write your answer again clearly.'

Levelling the children

Add together the marks from the oral and mental test and the oral and practical assessment. (Possible total: 20 marks)

Below Level 2	0 – 7 marks
Low Level 2	8 – 12 marks
Secure Level 2	13 – 15 marks
High Level 2	16 – 20 marks

This assessment reflects a child's performance in mental maths. When awarding an end-of-year teacher assessment level, teachers also need to consider a child's performance on periodic and day-to-day assessments across all learning objectives.

Test 1: Mental maths assessment

Part 1: Oral and mental questions

Time: 20 minutes (both parts).

- Read questions no more than twice to the children.
- Allow five seconds for each answer.
- Answers to be recorded on the answer sheet on pages 98-99.
- One mark per question: 15 marks total.

Resources

A ball; three containers (A, B, C) of differing sizes, with only one (A) holding more than a litre.

	Question	Answer
1	What number is one more than 124?	125
2	Three hundred and twenty-six – how many tens?	2 tens
3	Find the difference between 43 and 37.	6
4	*(Hold up a ball.)* What is this shape? (Tick the correct shape.)	sphere
5	I have £1. A comic costs 45p. How much change will I get?	55p
6	*(Use containers.)* Which of these containers would hold more than a litre?	A
7	How many hours are there in one day?	24
8	When I doubled a number the answer was 14. What was the number?	7
9	I need 28 books for Class 2. If a box holds ten books, how many boxes do I need?	3
10	I am thinking of a shape. It has five straight sides and no right angles. What is it?	pentagon
11	What is 6×5?	30
12	I start watching a television programme at 4:45. It finishes half an hour later. What time will it be?	5:15
13	What is ten less than 63?	53
14	I have eight sweets. I eat one quarter of them. How many do I have left?	6
15	$4 \times 5 = 20$. Use these numbers to make a division sentence.	$20 \div 4 = 5$ or $20 \div 5 = 4$

End of test

Name   Date

Test 1: Mental maths assessment

Part 1: Oral and mental assessment answer sheet (1 of 2)

	Answer	Mark
1		
2		
3		
4	cube ☐ pyramid ☐ sphere ☐	
5		
6		
7		
8		

Name   Date

Test 1: Mental maths assessment

Part 1: Oral and mental assessment answer sheet (2 of 2)

	Answer	Mark
9		
10		
11		
12		
13		
14		
15	4 × 5 =20	
End of test	Total	

Test 1: Mental maths assessment

Part 2: Oral and practical assessment

- Instructions and answers to be given orally to groups of no more than four children.
- One mark per question: 5 marks total.

Resources

Selection of regular 2D (paper) shapes (eg squares, rectangles, triangles, circles); numeral cards 50-100; page from a calendar with a one-month view; four analogue clocks; water; transparent litre measuring jug.

	Question	Mark
16	*Use 2D shapes.* Give two different shapes to each child. Ask each child in turn, to fold one of their shapes in half exactly and to fold the other shape into quarters.	1 mark
17	*Use numeral cards.* Give each child four cards. Ask each child to order their cards, from smallest to largest. Next, ask each child to read their cards. Finally, for each child, choose a card and ask them to give the next three numbers.	1 mark
18	*Use the calendar.* Place the calendar in the middle of the table. Start by asking general questions to introduce the calendar: What month is this? How many days are there in this month? How do you know? Then, in turn ask: Child A: What day is the 24th? Child B: How many Sundays are there in this month? Child C: What day was the 2nd? Child D: What day would the first day of the next month fall on?	1 mark
19	*Use the analogue clocks.* Ask each child in turn to show different times on their clock and then answer a question: Child A: 6:45 - What time will it be in 15 minutes? Child B: 4:15 - What time will it be in half an hour? Child C: 12:30 - What time will it be in 45 minutes? Child D: 4:45 - What time will it be in half an hour?	1 mark
20	*Use the litre measuring jug and water.* Ask each child to fill the jug to different capacities. Child A: 500ml; Child B: 300 ml; Child C: 1 litre; Child D: 800ml.	1 mark
End of test	**Total**	5 marks

Test 1: Mental maths assessment

Part 2: Oral and practical teacher's observation sheet

- This space can be used to record teacher's observations of pupil performance and marks gained.
- Make 'best fit' judgements when awarding marks. There are a total of 5 marks.

Name: _____

Question	Assessment outcome	Mark
16	• Folds one shape in half. • Folds one shape into quarters. (1 mark)	
17	• Orders four number cards. • Reads four number cards. • Identifies smallest/largest number. • Says next three numbers. (1 mark)	
18	• Extracts information from a calendar. (1 mark)	
19	• Shows the time on an analogue clock to 15-minute intervals. • Works out time intervals. (1 mark)	
20	• Fills a capacity jug to nearest 100ml. (1 mark)	
End of test	**Total**	

Level 3: Oral and mental assessments

Teachers' notes

Time: 20 minutes for each complete paper.

- Children should sit so that they cannot see each other's work.
- Do not explain questions or read numbers to the children.
- The test may be administered to groups of children or to the whole class.
- There are 20 marks available for each paper.
- Less confident learners could give their answers orally to a teaching assistant or other adult who could record their answers.

Delivering the tests

- Read each question to the children twice.
- Allow five seconds for each of the first 15 questions and ten seconds for each of the last five questions.
- Answers to be recorded on the answer sheets provided.
- One mark per question: 20 marks total.

Say to the children:

'I am going to read some questions for you to answer. I will read each question twice. You will have five seconds to answer some questions and ten seconds to answer some questions at the end of the test.'

'For most of the questions you will write your answer in a box.' [Show example.]

'For some questions you may need to tick the right answer.'

'If you make a mistake, you should cross it out and write your answer again clearly.'

Levelling the children

Add up the marks.
(Possible total: 20 marks)

Below Level 3	0 - 7 marks
Low Level 3	8 - 12 marks
Secure Level 3	13 - 15 marks
High Level 3	16 - 20 marks

This assessment reflects a child's performance in mental maths. When awarding an end-of-year teacher assessment level, teachers also need to consider a child's performance on periodic and day-to-day assessments over all learning objectives.

Test 1: Mental maths assessment

Oral and mental questions (page 1 of 2)

Time: 20 minutes

- Read each question twice to the children.
- Answers to be recorded on the answer sheet on pages 105–106.
- One mark per question: 20 marks total.
- Allow five seconds for each answer for questions 1–15; allow ten seconds for questions 16–20.

	Question	Answer
1	Write the number six thousand and forty-two.	6042
2	Calculate 65 + 21.	86
3	I have £1.00. I spend 76p. How much do I have left?	24p
4	*(Look at the fractions.)* Tick the fraction that is the same as $^6/_8$.	$^3/_4$
5	I have 246p. What is that in pounds and pence?	£2.46
6	I am thinking of a number. I double it and then add 10. My answer is 26. What was my number?	8
7	What do we call angles that are less than 90°?	acute
8	What is 8 × 3?	24
9	*(Look at the net.)* Tick the 3D shape that this net will make.	cuboid
10	How many centimetres are there in 4.5 metres?	450cm
11	*(Look at the clock.)* What time is it?	11.05 (or five past 11)
12	I am thinking of a number between 30 and 39. It is a multiple of 4 and also a multiple of 6. What number could it be?	36
13	*(Look at the coins.)* How much money is there?	£3.73

Test 1: Mental maths assessment

Oral and mental questions (page 2 of 2)

14	Amy is 163 centimetres tall. What is that to the nearest 10 centimetres?	160cm
15	What is the perimeter of an equilateral triangle if one side is 9cm long?	27cm
16	A square tile has an area of 100 square centimetres. What is the length of one of its sides?	10cm
17	If I practise reading for 15 minutes every night for a week, how long will I have spent reading?	1¾ hours, 1 hour 45 minutes or 105 minutes
18	*(Look at the Carroll diagram.)* Look at the shapes of the numerals in the diagram. Tick the number that is in the wrong place.	7
19	There are 32 counters. Half of them are blue and a quarter of them are red. The rest are green. How many are green?	8
20	The temperature during the day is 14°C. At night it is 20° colder. What is the night-time temperature?	-6°C

End of test

Name	Date

Test 1: Mental maths assessment

Part 1: Oral and mental assessment answer sheet (1 of 2)

	Answer			Mark
1				
2				
3				
4	$\frac{2}{3}$	$\frac{3}{4}$	$\frac{2}{5}$	
5				
6				
7				
8				
9	cube ☐ cuboid ☐ rectangle ☐			
10				
11				

Name	Date

Test 1: Mental maths assessment

Part 1: Oral and mental assessment answer sheet (2 of 2)

	Answer	Mark
12		
13		
14		
15		
16		
17		
18		
19		
20		

For question 18:

	Straight lines	No straight lines
Curved lines	5	3
No curved lines	4	7

End of test

	Total	

Test 2: Mental maths assessment

Oral and mental questions (page 1 of 2)

Time: 20 minutes
- Read each question twice to the children.
- Answers to be recorded on the answer sheet on pages 109–110.
- One mark per question: 20 marks total.
- Allow five seconds for each answer for questions 1–15; allow ten seconds for questions 16–20.

	Question	Answer
1	What number is one hundred more than 674?	774
2	What is the difference between 52 and 47?	5
3	A packet of crisps costs 40p. How many can I buy for £2.40?	6
4	*(Look at the shape.)* Tick the correct name.	octagon
5	How many months are there in a year?	12
6	Carrots are 64p per kilogram. How much is half a kilogram?	32p
7	What is 9 × 4?	36
8	*(Look at the shape.)* How many faces does the shape have?	6
9	Sam weighs 32 kilograms. How many grams is that?	32,000 grams
10	We start school at 9.05 and go for assembly at 9.55. How long is the first lesson?	50 minutes
11	I am facing south and turn anti-clockwise 90 degrees. Tick the direction I am now facing.	east
12	*(Look at the shape.)* Tick the correct name.	equilateral triangle

Test 2: Mental maths assessment

Oral and mental questions (page 2 of 2)

13	*(Look at the decimals.)* Tick the greatest number.	1.6
14	A multiple of 3 must be an odd number. True or false? Tick the right answer.	false
15	Each side of a regular pentagon measures eight centimetres. What is the total length of all its sides?	40cm
16	There are 27 children in my class. One third of them are girls. How many are boys?	18
17	*(Look at the table.)* How many fewer children liked plain than spring onion crisps?	13
18	Tom has 1 litre of water. He pours out 350 millilitres. How much water is left?	650ml
19	I am thinking of a multiple of 5. I double it and add 4. My answer is 64. What was my number?	30
20	Five apples cost 67p. How much does each apple cost to the nearest penny?	13p

End of test

Name   Date

Test 2: Mental maths assessment

Oral and mental assessment answer sheet (page 1 of 2)

	Answer	Mark
1		
2		
3		
4	octagon ☐ hexagon ☐ pentagon ☐	
5		
6		
7		
8		
9		
10		
11	north ☐ south ☐ east ☐ west ☐	

Name   Date

Test 2: Mental maths assessment

Oral and mental assessment answer sheet (page 2 of 2)

	Answer	Mark
12	right-angled triangle ☐ equilateral triangle ☐	
13	1.06 ☐ 1.6 ☐ 1.16 ☐	
14	true ☐ false ☐	
15		
16		
17		

For question 17:

Type of crisps	Number of children
Plain	15
Salt and vinegar	19
Spring onion	28
Smokey bacon	13
Sweet chilli	5

	Answer	Mark
18		
19		
20		
End of test	Total	

Mental maths teacher record sheet

Teacher's name: _____

Name of starter	PNS objectives covered	Block/unit	Date activity was used

SCHOLASTIC

Also available in this series:

100 MATHS ASSESSMENT LESSONS Y1
ISBN 978-1407-10183-5

100 MATHS ASSESSMENT LESSONS Y2
ISBN 978-1407-10184-2

100 MATHS ASSESSMENT LESSONS Y3
ISBN 978-1407-10185-9

100 MATHS ASSESSMENT LESSONS Y4
ISBN 978-1407-10192-7

100 MATHS ASSESSMENT LESSONS Y5
ISBN 978-1407-10193-4

100 MATHS ASSESSMENT LESSONS Y6
ISBN 978-1407-10194-1

100 MATHS FRAMEWORK LESSONS Y1
ISBN 978-0439-94546-2

100 MATHS FRAMEWORK LESSONS Y2
ISBN 978-0439-94547-9

100 MATHS FRAMEWORK LESSONS Y3
ISBN 978-0439-94548-6

100 MATHS FRAMEWORK LESSONS Y4
ISBN 978-0439-94549-3

100 MATHS FRAMEWORK LESSONS Y5
ISBN 978-0439-94550-9

100 MATHS FRAMEWORK LESSONS Y6
ISBN 978-0439-94551-6

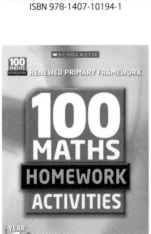

100 MATHS HOMEWORK ACTIVITIES Y1
ISBN 978-1407-10216-0

100 MATHS HOMEWORK ACTIVITIES Y2
ISBN 978-1407-10217-7

100 MATHS HOMEWORK ACTIVITIES Y3
ISBN 978-1407-10218-4

100 MATHS HOMEWORK ACTIVITIES Y4
ISBN 978-1407-10219-1

100 MATHS HOMEWORK ACTIVITIES Y5
ISBN 978-1407-10220-7

100 MATHS HOMEWORK ACTIVITIES Y6
ISBN 978-1407-10221-4

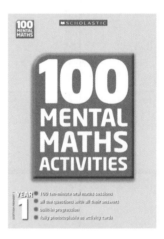

100 MENTAL MATHS ACTIVITIES Y1
ISBN 9781407114156

100 MENTAL MATHS ACTIVITIES Y2
ISBN 9781407114163

100 MENTAL MATHS ACTIVITIES Y3
ISBN 9781407114170

100 MENTAL MATHS ACTIVITIES Y4
ISBN 9781407114187

100 MENTAL MATHS ACTIVITIES Y5
ISBN 9781407114194

100 MENTAL MATHS ACTIVITIES Y6
ISBN 9781407114200

For further information, visit www.scholastic.co.uk/classpet